1970

SATIRE

SATIRE

Modes of Literature Series

Edited by

Ashley Brown
John L. Kimmey

University of South Carolina

Charles E. Merrill Publishing Company
Columbus, Ohio
A Bell & Howell Company

Library of Congress Catalog Number: 69-10743

69 70 71 72 73 / 10 9 8 7 6 5 4 3 2 1

Printed in the United States of America

Preface

The *Modes of Literature* Series differs from most anthologies introducing
college students to literature by stressing synthesis as well as analysis. It
organizes stories, poems, and plays into modes rather than into fiction,
poetry, and drama. The purpose of this arrangement is to unify the selections in an organic and meaningful way so that they relate to each other and
provide a cohesive approach to a variety of works from American, English,
and Continental literatures.

We define a mode both as a mood or attitude which the writer assumes
toward his subject and the form or manner in which the subject reveals itself.
During the 18th Century, for instance, when satire was an important mode,
a poet or prose writer searched the world around him for subjects to attack
or ridicule. His mood could be bitter, his attitude ironic, his tone either
facetious or angry. To express his views he might use the mock-epic, such
as Alexander Pope did in *The Rape of the Lock*, or the manner of a travel
book which Voltaire adopted for *Candide*.

The major modes of literature are epic, tragedy, comedy, tragicomedy,
satire, and romance. All of these are represented in the five volumes of this
anthology with the exception of epic. Limitations of space obviously make
it impossible to reprint a long poem such as the *Aeneid*. As for the novel, we
do not regard it as a separate mode, for it might be epical, tragic, comic,
satiric, romantic, or a combination of these. Throughout the five volumes
our emphasis is on fairly long works, although we include a number of short
poems and stories. Many of these long works are familiar, part of the cul-
tural heritage of the Western World. Their association with a mode, however, places several of them in a new light. Wordsworth's "Michael" is an
example of a poem that read in terms of tragedy becomes a stronger and
more complex work than it is generally thought to be. Less familiar selections
such as Chekhov's "Ward No. 6," Aldous Huxley's "Nuns at Luncheon,"

Elizabeth Bishop's "The Burglar of Babylon," and Robert Lowell's *Benito Cereno* add a freshness often absent from texts that usually rely on the tried and the conventional.

There are a number of advantages to our approach. Instead of viewing a literary work as having only a tenuous connection with the one preceding or following it in an anthology, we see it as belonging to a diverse group of poems, plays, and stories that exhibit the common characteristics of one of the major modes. This mode, then, becomes the precise focus of attention. In a satire, for instance, not only does the student analyze *The Misanthrope* and Swift's "A Modest Proposal" but through them and other works he develops an understanding of what satire is, how it has evolved, who are some of its important writers, and what kinds of experience it presents in different ages. While there is much to be said for restricting the study of literature to a concern with style and form, or centering it on significant social and moral themes, either method in itself tends to be one-sided. Our approach engages the student simultaneously in a formal interpretation of literature and a consideration of the vital themes it embodies.

Although the sequence of tragedy, comedy, tragicomedy, satire, and romance is the one we recommend, the five modes can be taken up separately and in any order. Each volume is self-sufficient and does not depend on any other. Occasionally, however, there are references in the introduction or a question to another mode, but these are kept to a minimum. Their aim is to show how the modes touch and cross despite their lines of division.

The selections in this particular volume do not in any sense attempt to represent the entire history of satire. The introductory essay largely fulfills this function. Its purpose also is to suggest approaches to the poems, stories, and plays included and to stimulate the reader to arrive at his own conclusions about their satiric nature.

We wish to thank Betty Trueblood for her assistance in preparing this manuscript. Her efficiency is exceeded only by her abundant good humor. We also wish to express our gratitude to Jane Kimmey for her suggestions and her encouragement.

A. B.

J. L. K.

Contents

SATIRE

Satire: Introduction

Satire is one of the oldest literary modes, but it has not always been admired in the way that tragedy and romance and even comedy have been. The satirist, one sometimes hears, is destructive and malicious; people who are happy with the world as it is may find him disagreeable. And indeed the two greatest English satirists, Swift and Pope, were not the most pleasant of men. But the editors of this anthology consider satire an important and exhilarating way of dealing with human experience, and no student of literature should overlook its variety and power and often its sheer enjoyment. Over the centuries it has appealed on occasion to many literary men, for instance Chaucer and Shakespeare. In our age we can see it in the work of James Joyce and T. S. Eliot, writers who fit into other literary modes more conveniently. The satiric impulse is certainly widespread today. Very likely the contemporary public is more receptive to it than the 19th Century public. Much of our art today is frankly intellectual in its appeal (or at least it is concerned with the clash of ideas), and satire is perhaps the literary mode most relevant to this situation.

Although the early history of satire is partly a matter of speculation, we can briefly indicate how it has evolved. The first satirist we know about, Archilochus (7th Century B.C.), was a Greek poet who followed Homer. Werner Jaeger, a famous Hellenist of the last generation, said that the poetry of Archilochus "was born of the need of the free individual to see and solve the problem of human life outside the mystic content of epic poetry, which had hitherto been the only sphere in which it could be posed or answered." This remark suggests something about satirists generally. They often follow the "heroic" writers like Homer and Virgil, or Spenser and Milton, and some of their most characteristic thrusts have been delivered at the pretensions of heroism.

In the ancient world the term *satire* did not come into being immediately. But it is almost certainly derived from the Latin *satura*, meaning a "mixture" or "medley" as derived from *satura lanx*, a bowl of first fruits. (Note that the Greeks did not have the word.) Satire thus seems to have had this "mixed" quality much of the time: verse and prose, sublime and vulgar styles, the effect of an improvisation. It is worth remarking here that writers

1

and critics in the Middle Ages and the Renaissance mistakenly thought that *satire* was derived from the Greek *satyr* and often acted on the assumption that the mode should be "rough" and even obscene in its effects.

Although the Romans established the forms of satire which we have inherited, the characteristic tone of this mode can be seen earlier in the plays of Aristophanes, an Athenian Greek who found much to attack in the public life of his city-state. Some of his plays, such as the *Lysistrata* (an attack on the folly of war) and *The Clouds* (an attack on the Socratic school of philosophy), are still acted with success, and a modern audience does not seem to object at all to the occasional indecencies which might have shocked our grandparents.

But classical satire did not develop in this dramatic form. Following Aristophanes, the Greek satirist Menippus (ca. 340-ca. 270 B.C.) lent his name to one of the major forms eventually perfected by the Romans, and Menippean satire is still the name we give it. How can we define this? A Menippean satire is essentially a prose narrative which usually contains some verse, often descending to the popular and coarse in its attack on folly. There is an outstanding fragmentary example in Roman literature which is widely read today: The *Satyricon* by Petronius Arbiter. This *habitué* of Nero's court has given us an extraordinary picture of the dissolute Rome of his generation. His narrative is typical in its loose plotting (Menippean satire usually has this effect of the improvisation), but here and there we have entire scenes which anticipate the technique of the modern novel. Menippean satire, then, is the term which we can later apply in an extended sense to narratives such as *Don Quixote* and *Candide*, with their plots based on accumulations of adventures.

The other kind of satire which the Romans perfected might be called simply formal verse satire. The Roman poets Horace and Juvenal are chiefly associated with this development, and most of the classic satires in English poetry are based to some extent on their practice. Horace, who lived during the "golden age" of Augustus Caesar, and who was evidently a happy man, censured follies and vices with a "fine raillery," as John Dryden called it. The special tone of Horace's work has been admired and imitated by such English poets as Marvell and Pope, and indeed his influence on English poetry has been extensive. In this anthology we have included both his famous satire on city life and Juvenal's Satire III, an attack on the vices and dangers of imperial Rome by one who was doubtless led to his disillusionment by sad experience. Juvenal, who came more than a century after Horace, saw the Empire in its decline. For his fictional situation he has himself addressed by Umbricius, a bitter citizen who is about to desert Rome for Naples. (The student who wishes to follow up Juvenal's Satire III should read Dr. Johnson's "London," which is directly modelled on it.) This kind of denunciation—the typical Juvenalian tone—is something we often find in satire, and Shakespeare, in *Timon of Athens*, manages to sustain it for much of a full-length play.

Although satire is sometimes identified with comedy—and certainly it can be very funny—it is basically concerned with exposing some flaw or excess. Indeed, some satire (Dr. Johnson's "London" for instance) contains no humor. But the ways of exposing flaws and excesses are many, and the satirist can adopt various stances, including the playful and witty as well as the vitriolic. Juvenal is wise in putting his denunciation of Rome into the speech of a poor decent citizen who can endure no more of the corruption; the poet thus "distances" himself from his own feelings and avoids the self-pity which is so unattractive. Satire, then, ranges from almost open invective to whimsical play. The satirist differs from the comic artist, however, in not quite accepting the world as it is. A case in point is Byron's *Don Juan*. Although this long comic poem contains some incidental satire, Byron really has no sustained indictment of society here, and he gives the impression of delighting in its incongruities. On the other hand, in an early (and inferior) work, *English Bards and Scotch Reviewers*, he turns sarcastically against the literary critics who he feels are obstructing young poets, and the result is unquestionably satire. Returning to Juvenal once more, we might observe his *fiction*, his make-believe situation, as a way of mounting his attack. This is important. The true satirist, no matter how violent his feelings, usually tries to get at his target *indirectly*. Otherwise we have only diatribe.

In mentioning Archilochus, who followed Homer, we said that satire tends to be anti-heroic. But this does not mean that the satirist is frivolous (even when his manner is an assumed frivolity). He is usually a disillusioned moralist, and he is unlikely to accept big ideas and ideals without question. Aristophanes had good reason to write *Lysistrata*, and Shakespeare treated the same anti-war theme more comprehensively in *Troilus and Cressida*, the finest dramatic satire in English. The student can see a smaller and brilliant example of the anti-heroic in *The Rape of the Lock*. This poem was written in the aftermath of Milton's *Paradise Lost*, the most impressive epic or "heroic" poem in our tradition. The climactic part of the epic has Eve succumbing to temptation and eating the forbidden fruit; hence the Fall of Man. Much of the epic "machinery" (the angels and their activities) is there to make the event in the Garden of Eden seem vast in its importance. Pope, himself a Roman Catholic and an admirer of Milton, wittily uses certain phases of Milton's poem for satirical purposes. His climactic incident is the loss of a vain society belle's lock of hair. By surrounding this trivial incident with a considerable array of "machinery" (in this case a small army of flimsy sylphs), Pope makes the supernatural devices of Milton's poem seem ridiculous—at least in the social setting of 18th Century London. We may say, then, that this is a first-rate example of *literary* satire, what we call a mock epic, in which a certain kind of grand style is turned against itself. A good satirist is almost invariably a good rhetorician; that is, he knows how to manipulate styles to witty advantage.

Critics who are suspicious of satirists claim that their poetry (or prose) is "intellectual." One could hardly claim, however, that Pope is more intellectual than Milton or even Shakespeare. *King Lear* is profoundly intellectual. But satire does seem aimed at the critical intelligence of the audience. The reader, that is to say, must be able to see the discrepancy between style and subject. Of all the great English satirists, Swift perhaps makes the most demands on the reader's judgment—it is a moral judgment that is at issue. In the famous last book of *Gulliver's Travels* we are presented with two alternatives: the repulsive Yahoos (the representation of men) and the beautiful Houyhnhnms, the "reasonable" horses who gain so much by the comparison. It perhaps takes a sophisticated reader to see that the kind of "reason" that we get in these horses is limited and unworthy of the truly enlightened. Swift's real moral standard is never directly stated: the reader must locate that for himself, given the alternatives. Similarly in "A Modest Proposal" the reader must see the difference between the horrible attitude he is being asked to endorse and some true moral standard. The tone of the essay is so "reasonable," and the modern reader may consider overpopulation such a danger, that he could get well into the satire before he realized that he was in effect approving a mass-murder. What Swift wants to do is shock the public into awareness.

Satire is not an exclusive mode. It operates in various forms. *Gulliver*, for instance, is in one sense a romance because it deals in the improbable. But it is primarily a satire. *Candide* likewise is a loosely plotted narrative which suggests the romance; but as the critic Northrop Frye has pointed out, ". . . it is not primarily concerned with the exploits of heroes, but relies on the free play of intellectual fancy and the kind of humorous observation that produces caricature." We could say the same thing about George Orwell's *Animal Farm*, a beast fable adapted for modern political satire. Molière's *The Misanthrope* has all the surface tone of a comedy of manners,[1] but the play is a sustained attack on the hypocrisies and insincerities of a society which, although aristocratic and Parisian, is not unlike our own. The very inflation of Alceste's style of speech often exposes his pretensions. The play has also been called tragic because of the "noble,

---

[1] A comedy of manners is a witty play dealing with the manners and morals of a sophisticated society. The characters are types, such as clever young men, jealous husbands, fops. The dialogue is in the form of brilliant repartee. The main situation often concerns a pair of amoral lovers who reflect the brittle social world of the day. Such drama has been popular in France and England since the 17th Century.

heroic side" of Alceste and the fact that he is a lonely figure in a world set against him.

In the case of verse satire we should not underestimate the importance of form. For instance, most of the classic satirists in French and English for almost two centuries (from 1600 to 1800) wrote in couplets. This is true of writers as different as La Fontaine and Swift and Molière in *The Misanthrope* (here beautifully translated by Richard Wilbur). The couplet, and in particular the heroic couplet,[2] has an epigrammatic quality which makes it especially suitable for satire: it delivers a concentration of effect which perhaps no other verse form can do. Pope in *The Rape of the Lock* thus epitomizes an entire society in four lines:

> The hungry judges soon the sentence sign,
> And wretches hang that jurymen may dine;
> The merchant from th' exchange returns in peace,
> And the long labors of the toilet cease.

This kind of terse elegance is often associated with the comedy of manners, but the satirist (especially in English, a language not so precise as French) deliberately uses it as a blunt instrument. Thus William Blake, who inherited the 18th Century instinct for the epigram, wrote:

> Pity would be no more
> If we did not make somebody Poor

There are, however, other forms which the poet-satirist can use. Shakespeare, for example, in Sonnet 130, is satirizing the form itself, which in the Renaissance was virtually identified with a certain kind of sentiment about love—the Petrarchan convention of extravagantly praising one's mistress. Donne's "Song" is likewise anti-Petrarchan. Burns and John Betjeman use conventional forms of prayers in their dramatic monologues.[3] Because Betjeman is a contemporary poet, perhaps we can see (or rather we should hear) that the singsong rhythms spoken by his worshipper are mechanical and open to suspicion in themselves. To repeat: a good satirist knows how to manipulate styles to witty advantage.

Although, as we have stated, the impulse to satirize is a powerful force in our culture today, a number of critics believe that the mode is difficult to practice. Among them is W. H. Auden, preëminently a comic poet, who recently made this pertinent observation:

---

[2] The heroic couplet is a pair of rimed iambic pentameter lines that are usually end-stopped. There is a marked pause in the middle of each line and symmetrical phrasing in each half of the line so that the couplet often contains balanced sentences marked by parallelism and antithesis.

[3] A dramatic monologue is a poem in which a character speaks in a dramatic situation and reveals, often unintentionally, his innermost nature.

Satire flourishes in a homogeneous society where satirist and audience share the same view as to how normal people can be expected to behave, and in times of relative stability and contentment, for satire cannot deal with serious evil and suffering. In an age like our own, it cannot flourish except in intimate circles as an expression of private feuds: in public life the evils and sufferings are so serious that satire seems trivial and the only possible kind of attack is prophetic denunciation.

It is true that our literary period is not a time of "relative stability" and that the satiric impulse is rarely sustained as in the greatest works of Pope and Swift. And Auden is probably right in maintaining that the satirist and his audience no longer agree on standards. For instance, a writer like Vladimir Nabokov in *Lolita* is apt to be misunderstood by many of his readers, a fact which makes his attack on the social and sexual mores of our society all the more savage. Nevertheless, the satirist today has had some successes in dealing with major topics as witness Betjeman's "Westminster Abbey" which exposes the rather dubious piety of Englishmen in time of war. Though the poet expresses more amusement than outrage, he makes his point in an effective manner by means of irony. Satirists who deal with other aspects of public life have done much more. There is, for instance, the anti-utopian satire. This is a classic theme—one can find it in Aristophanes and Swift and in a sense in Voltaire's *Candide*. Aldous Huxley's *Brave New World* and Orwell's *Animal Farm* continue this tradition, and Orwell's book at least seems on the way to becoming a small classic itself. In the United States, where the short story has flourished, several writers have dealt sharply with what might be called the decay of the community. J. F. Powers in "Blue Island" presents a travesty of what a community should be. Is he far from the truth? Does the reader notice or lament those human values which are missing? Flannery O'Connor in "Everything That Rises Must Converge" takes up the moral issues of racism which have run through American society in late years. What is her point of view? It is never stated. Like Swift, she forces the reader to create a moral standard against which to measure these strange behaviors she portrays.

There is finally one problem of satire which Auden touches on: what he calls "an expression of private feuds." We might restate it in this way: satire often arises from an immediate occasion, the indignation that a writer feels in confronting a particular folly. For this reason, the danger always seems to be that the occasion is only a passing one and the satire is therefore not of permanent interest. But the best satirists transcend the occasion—for instance Swift in "A Modest Proposal"—and make us see that a single instance of stupidity, personal or communal, can represent much more than itself. Such, we think, is the case with each of the satires in this book.

Suggestions for Further Reading

Elliott, Robert C. *The Power of Satire.* Princeton: The Princeton University Press, 1960.

Guicharnaud, Jacques, *Molière, A Collection of Critical Essays.* Englewood Cliffs, N. J.: Prentice-Hall, Inc., 1964.

Highet, Gilbert. *Juvenal the Satirist.* Oxford: Clarendon Press, 1954.

Jack, Ian. *Augustan Satire.* Oxford: Clarendon Press, 1961.

Kernan, Alvin. *The Cankered Muse: Satire of the English Renaissance.* New Haven: Yale University Press, 1959.

_____. *The Plot of Satire.* New Haven: Yale University Press, 1965.

Lewis, Wyndham. *Men Without Art.* New York: Russell and Russell, 1964.

Rosenheim, Edward W. *Swift and the Satirist's Art.* Chicago: University of Chicago Press, 1963.

Russell, John and Ashley Brown. *Satire: A Critical Anthology.* Cleveland and New York: World Publishing Company, 1967.

Worcester, David. *The Art of Satire.* Cambridge, Mass.: Harvard University Press, 1940.

Horace (*65-8* B.C.)

The Town Mouse and the Country Mouse

From *The Second Book of Satires*

ADAPTED FROM THE TRANSLATION BY SIR THEODORE MARTIN

My prayers with this I used to charge:
A piece of land not over large,
Wherein there should a garden be,
A clear spring flowing ceaselessly,
And where, to crown the whole, there should
Be found a patch of growing wood.
All this, and more, the gods have sent,
And I am heartily content.
    O son of Maia,[1] that I may
These blessings keep is all I pray.   10
If never by craft or base design
I've swelled what little store is mine,
Nor mean it ever shall be wrecked
Through my own failing or neglect;
If never from my lips a word
Shall drop of prayers so absurd
As, "Had I but that little nook,
Next to my field, that spoils its look!"
Or, "Would some lucky chance unfold
To me a crock of hidden gold,   20
As to the man, whom Hercules
Enriched and settled at his ease,
Who, with the treasure he had found,
Bought for himself the very ground

---

[1] Mercury, the god of gain, and the protector of poets.

Which he before for hire had tilled!"
If I with gratitude am filled
For what I have—by this I dare
Implore you to fulfil my prayer,
That you with fatness will endow
My little herd of cattle now,   30
And all things else their lord may own,
Except what wits he has alone,
And be, as heretofore, my chief
Protector, guardian, and relief!
    So, when from town and all its ills
I to my perch among the hills
Retreat, what better theme to choose
Than satire for my homely Muse?
No cruel ambition wastes me there,
No, nor the south wind's leaden air,   40
Nor Autumn's pestilential breath,
With victims feeding hungry death.
Sire of the morn, or if you prefer,
The name of Janus to your ear,[2]
Through whom whate'er to man is dear,
(So willed the gods for man's estate),
Do you my verse initiate!
At Rome you hurry me away
To bail my friend: "Quick, no delay,
Or some one—could worse luck befall you?—   50
Will in the kindly task forestall you."
So go I must, although the wind
Is north and killingly unkind,
Or snow, in thickly-falling flakes,
The wintry day more wintry makes.
And when, articulate and clear,
I've spoken what may cost me dear,
Elbowing the crowd that round me close,
I'm sure to crush somebody's toes.
"What's up, where are you pushing to?   60
What would you have, you madman, you?
You think that you, now, I daresay,

---

2 Janus, a divinity specially dear to the Latin race, presided over not only the opening of every year and every month, but also of every day. Prayers were offered to him
every morning.

May push whatever stops your way,
When you are to Maecenas bound!"[3]
Sweet, sweet, as honey is the sound,
I won't deny, of that last speech,
But then no sooner do I reach
The gloomy Esquiline,[4] than straight
Buzz, buzz around me runs the prate
Of people pestering me with cares,   70
All about other men's affairs.
"Roscius, according to report,
Expects by seven you'll be in court!"
"The scriveners, worthy Horace, pray,
You'll not forget they meet to-day,
Upon a point both grave and new,
One touching the whole body, too."[5]
"Do get Maecenas, do, to sign
This application here of mine!"
"Well, well, I'll try." "You can with ease   80
Arrange it, if you only please."
        Close on eight years it now must be,
Since first Maecenas numbered me
Among his friends, as one to take
Out driving with him, and to make
The confidant of trifles, say,
Like this, "What is the time of day?"
"The Thracian Bantam, would you bet
On him, or on the Syrian Pet?"[6]
"These chilly mornings will do harm,   90
If you don't mind to wrap up warm"
Such gossip as without a fear
One drops into the leakiest ear.
Yet all this time has envy's glance
On me looked more and more askance.
From mouth to mouth such comments run:
"Our friend indeed is Fortune's son.
Why, there he was, we all recall,

---

[3] Horace's patron.
[4] Where Maecenas lived in Rome.
[5] Horace had belonged, if indeed he did not still belong, to the "*ordo*" or guild of "*Scribæ*," and, trusting to his influence in high quarters, they were anxious he should attend a meeting in which some matters of importance to the interests of the body was to be discussed.
[6] Gladiators.

Beside Maecenas playing ball."
 Some chilling news through lane and street   100
Spreads from the Forum. All I meet
Accost me thus—"Dear friend, you're so
Close to the gods, that you must know:
About the Dacians, have you heard
Any fresh tidings?" "Not a word!"
"You're always jesting!" "Now may all
The gods confound me, great and small,
If I have heard one word!" "Well, well,
But you at any rate can tell
If Caesar means the lands, which he   110
Has promised to his troops, shall be
Selected from Italian ground,
Or in Sicily be found?"
And when I swear, as well I can,
That I know nothing, for a man
Of silence rare and most discreet
They cry me up to all the street.
 Thus do my wasted days slip by,
Not without many a wish and sigh.
Oh, when shall I the country see,   120
Its woodlands green? Oh, when be free,
With books of great old men, and sleep,
And hours of dreamy ease, to creep
Into oblivion sweet of life,
Its agitations and its strife?
When on my table shall be seen
Pythagoras's kin, the bean,[7]
And bacon, not too fat, embellish
My dish of greens, and give it relish?
Oh happy nights, oh feasts divine,   130
When, with the friends I love, I dine
At my own hearth-fire, and the meat
We leave gives my bluff slaves a treat!
No stupid laws our feasts control,
But each guest drains or leaves the bowl,
Precisely as he feels inclined.
If he be strong, and have a mind

---

[7] Referring to the popular opinion that Pythagoras and his disciples would not eat this vegetable, because in doing so they might be devouring their own flesh and blood—they believed in the transmigration of souls.

For seconds, good! if not, he's free
To sip his liquor leisurely.
And then the talk our banquet rouses!   140
Not gossip about our neighbours' houses,
Or if 'tis generally thought
That Lepos dances well or not?[8]
But what concerns us nearer, and
Is harmful not to understand,
Whether by wealth or worth, it's plain,
That men to happiness attain?
By what we're led to choose our friends,—
Regard for them, or our own ends?
In what does good consist, and what   150
Is the supremest form of that?
    My neighbor Cervius will strike in
With some old woman's tale, akin
To what we are discussing. Thus,
If some one recommends to us
Arellius' wealth, forgetting how
Much care it costs him, "Look you now,
Once on a time," he will begin,
"A country mouse received within
His humble cave a city brother,   160
As one old comrade would another.
A frugal mouse upon the whole,
But loved his friend, and had a soul,
And could be free and open-handed,
When hospitality demanded.
In brief, he did not spare his hoard
Of corn and peas, long carefully stored;
Raisins he brought, and scraps, to boot,
Half-gnawed, of bacon, which he put
With his own mouth before his guest,   170
In hopes, by offering his best
In such variety, he might
Persuade him to an appetite.
The city mouse, with languid eye,
Just picked a bit, then put it by;
Which with dismay the rustic saw,
As, stretched upon some stubbly straw,

---

8 Lepos was a celebrated mime, and spoke and acted as well as danced.

He munched at bran and common grits,
Not venturing on the dainty bits.
At length the town mouse: 'What,' says he,   180
'My good friend, can the pleasure be
Of grubbing here, on the backbone
Of a great crag with trees o'ergrown?
Who'd not to these wild woods prefer
The city, with its crowds and stir?
Then come with me to town; you'll ne'er
Regret the hour that took you there.
All earthly things draw mortal breath;
Nor great nor little can from death
Escape, and therefore, friend, be gay,   190
Enjoy life's good things while you may,
Remembering how brief the space
Allowed to you in any case.'
        His words struck home; and, light of heart,
The rustic didn't wait to start,
Timing their journey so they might
Reach town beneath the cloud of night,
Which was at its high noon, when they
To a rich mansion found their way,
Where shining ivory couches vied   200
With coverlets in scarlet dyed,
And where in baskets were amassed
The ruins of a great repast,
Which some few hours before had closed.
There, having first his friend disposed
Upon a purple cover, straight
The city mouse began to wait
With scraps upon his country brother,
Each scrap more dainty than another,
And all a servant's duty proffered,   210
First tasting everything offered.
        The guest, reclining there in state,
Rejoiced now in his new-found fate,
Over each fresh tidbit smacked his lips,
And broke into the merriest quips,
When suddenly a banging door
Shook host and guest into the floor.
From room to room they rushed aghast,
And almost fell down dead at last,

When loud through all the house came sounds—   220
The barking of colossal hounds.
    'Ho!' cried the country mouse. 'This kind
Of life is not for me, I find.
Give me my woods and cavern. There
At least I'm safe! And though both spare
And poor my food may be, rebel
I never will; so, fare you well!' "

Questions for Discussion

1. Why do you think Horace begins the poem with a prayer? How is it related to satire?

2. What are the chief complaints which Horace makes against Rome?

3. Does Horace seem altogether happy to be a friend of his famous patron Maecenas?

4. How does Horace dramatize the public life of Rome?

5. Why does Horace consider the conversation in the country superior to that in Rome?

6. Does the fable of the two mice reinforce Horace's ideas about true happiness?

7. Which of the two mice better exemplifies the ideal of hospitality?

8. To what extent is the poem a satire?

Juvenal (ca. 60 - ca. 140)

The Third Satire

Translated by Rolfe Humphries

AGAINST THE CITY OF ROME

Troubled because my old friend is going, I still must commend him
For his decision to settle down in the ghost town of Cumae,
Giving the Sibyl one citizen more. That's the gateway to Baiae
There, a pleasant shore, a delightful retreat. I'd prefer
Even a barren rock in that bay to the brawl of Subura.[1]
Where have we ever seen a place so dismal and lonely
We'd not be better off there, than afraid, as we are here, of fires,
Roofs caving in, and the thousand risks of this terrible city
Where the poets recite all through the dog days of August?

While they are loading his goods on one little four-wheeled wagon,   10
Here he waits, by the old archways which the aqueducts moisten.
This is where Numa,[2] by night, came to visit his goddess.
That once holy grove, its sacred spring, and its temple,
Now are let out to the Jews, if they have some straw and a basket.
Every tree, these days, has to pay rent to the people.
Kick the Muses out; the forest is swarming with beggars.
So we go down to Egeria's vale, with its modern improvements.
How much more close the presence would be, were there lawns by the
     water,
Turf to the curve of the pool, not this unnatural marble!

Umbricius has much on his mind. "Since there's no place in the city,"   20
He says, "For an honest man, and no reward for his labors,

Satire III by Juvenal, translated by Rolfe Humphries. Reprinted with permission of
Indiana University Press from *The Satires of Juvenal* by Rolfe Humphries.

[1] A busy street in central Rome.
[2] An ancestral priest-king; *his goddess*, Egeria.

15

Since I have less today than yesterday, since by tomorrow
That will have dwindled still more, I have made my decision. I'm going
To the place where, I've heard, Daedalus put off his wings,
While my white hair is still new, my old age in the prime of its
    straightness,
While my fate spinner still has yarn on her spool, while I'm able
Still to support myself on two good legs, without crutches.
Rome, good-bye! Let the rest stay in the town if they want to,
Fellows like A, B, and C, who make black white at their pleasure,
Finding it easy to grab contracts for rivers and harbors,   30
Putting up temples, or cleaning out sewers, or hauling off corpses,
Or, if it comes to that, auctioning slaves in the market.
Once they used to be hornblowers, working the carneys;
Every wide place in the road knew their puffed-out cheeks and their
    squealing.
Now they give shows of their own. Thumbs up! Thumbs down! And
    the killers
Spare or slay, and then go back to concessions for private privies.
Nothing they won't take on. Why not?—since the kindness of Fortune
(Fortune is out for laughs) has exalted them out of the gutter.

"What should I do in Rome? I am no good at lying.
If a book's bad, I can't praise it, or go around ordering copies.   40
I don't know the stars; I can't hire out as assassin
When some young man wants his father knocked off for a price; I
    have never
Studied the guts of frogs, and plenty of others know better
How to convey to a bride the gifts of the first man she cheats with.
I am no lookout for thieves, so I cannot expect a commission
On some governor's staff. I'm a useless corpse, or a cripple.
Who has a pull these days, except your yes men and stooges
With blackmail in their hearts, yet smart enough to keep silent?
No honest man feels in debt to those he admits to his secrets,
But your Verres[3] must love the man who can tattle on Verres   50
Any old time that he wants. Never let the gold of the Tagus,
Rolling under its shade, become so important, so precious
You have to lie awake, take bribes that you'll have to surrender,
Tossing in gloom, a threat to your mighty patron forever.

"Now let me speak of the race that our rich men dote on most fondly.
These I avoid like the plague, let's have no coyness about it.

---

[3] A politician in the old Republic, more than a century earlier.

Citizens, I can't stand a Greekized Rome. Yet what portion
Of the dregs of our town comes from Achaia[4] only?
Into the Tiber pours the silt, the mud of Orontes,[5]
Bringing its babble and brawl, its dissonant harps and its timbrels,   60
Bringing also the tarts who display their wares at the Circus.
Here's the place, if your taste is for hat-wearing whores, brightly
    colored!
What have they come to now, the simple souls from the country
Romulus used to know? They put on the *trechedipna*
(That might be called, in our tongue, their running-to-dinner outfit),
Pin on their *niketeria* (medals), and smell *ceromatic*
(Attar of wrestler). They come, trooping from Samos and Tralles,
Andros, wherever that is, Azusa and Cucamonga,[6]
Bound for the Esquiline or the hill we have named for the vineyard,
Termites, into great halls where they hope, some day, to be tyrants.   70
Desperate nerve, quick wit, as ready in speech as Isaeus,
Also a lot more long-winded. Look over there! See that fellow?
What do you take him for? He can be anybody he chooses,
Doctor of science or letters, a vet or a chiropractor,
Orator, painter, masseur, palmologist, tightrope walker.
If he is hungry enough, your little Greek stops at nothing.
Tell him to fly to the moon, and he runs right off for his space ship.
Who flew first? Some Moor, some Turk, some Croat, or some Slovene?
Not on your life, but a man from the very center of Athens.

"Should I not run away from these purple-wearing freeloaders?   80
Must I wait while they sign their names? Must their couches always be
    softer?
Stowaways, that's how they got here, in the plums and figs from
    Damascus.
I was here long before they were: my boyhood drank in the sky
Over the Aventine hill; I was nourished by Sabine olives.
Agh, what lackeys they are, what sycophants! See how they flatter
Some ignoramus's talk, or the looks of some horrible eyesore,
Saying some Ichabod Crane's long neck reminds them of muscles
Hercules strained when he lifted Antaeus aloft on his shoulders,
Praising some cackling voice that really sounds like a rooster's
When he's pecking a hen. We can praise the same objects that they do,   90
Only, they are believed. Does an actor do any better
Mimicking Thais, Alcestis, Doris without any clothes on?

---

4 Greece.
5 The river which flows through Antioch in the Near East.
6 *Samos . . . Cucamonga*, places in Greece.

It seems that a woman speaks, not a mask; the illusion is perfect
Down to the absence of bulge and the little cleft under the belly.
Yet they win no praise at home, for all of their talent.
Why?—Because Greece is a stage, and every Greek is an actor.
Laugh, and he splits his sides; weep, and his tears flow in torrents
Though he's not sad; if you ask for a little more fire in the winter
He will put on his big coat; if you say 'I'm hot,' he starts sweating.
We are not equals at all; he always has the advantage,   100
Able, by night or day, to assume, from another's expression,
This or that look, prepared to throw up his hands, to cheer loudly
If his friend gives a good loud belch or doesn't piss crooked,
Or if a gurgle comes from his golden cup when inverted
Straight up over his nose—a good deep swig, and no heeltaps!

"Furthermore, nothing is safe from his lust, neither matron nor virgin,
Not her affianced spouse, or the boy too young for the razor.
If he can't get at these, he would just as soon lay his friend's grandma.
(Anything, so he'll get in to knowing the family secrets!)
Since I'm discussing the Greeks, let's turn to their schools and
          professors,   110
The crimes of the hood and gown. Old Dr. Egnatius, informant,
Brought about the death of Barea, his friend and his pupil,
Born on that riverbank where the pinion of Pegasus landed.
No room here, none at all, for any respectable Roman
Where a Protogenes rules, or a Diphilus, or a Hermarchus,
Never sharing their friends—a racial characteristic!
Hands off! He puts a drop of his own, or his countryside's poison
Into his patron's ear, an ear which is only too willing
And I am kicked out of the house, and all my years of long service
Count for nothing. Nowhere does the loss of a client mean less.   120

"Let's not flatter ourselves. What's the use of our service?
What does a poor man gain by hurrying out in the nighttime,
All dressed up before dawn, when the praetor nags at his troopers
Bidding them hurry along to convey his respects to the ladies,
Barren, of course, like Albina, before any others can get there?
Sons of men freeborn give right of way to a rich man's
Slave; a crack, once or twice, at Calvina or Catiena[7]
Costs an officer's pay, but if you like the face of some floozy

---

[7] Prostitutes.

You hardly have money enough to make her climb down from her
    high chair.
Put on the stand, at Rome, a man with a record unblemished,   130
No more a perjurer than Numa was, or Metellus,
What will they question? His wealth, right away, and possibly, later,
(Only possibly, though) touch on his reputation.
'How many slaves does he feed? What's the extent of his acres?
How big are his platters? How many? What of his goblets and wine
    bowls?'
His word is as good as his bond—if he has enough bonds in his
    strongbox.
But a poor man's oath, even if sworn on all altars
All the way from here to the farthest Dodecanese island,
Has no standing in court. What has he to fear from the lightnings
Of the outraged gods? He has nothing to lose; they'll ignore him.   140

"If you're poor, you're a joke, on each and every occasion.
What a laugh, if your cloak is dirty or torn, if your toga
Seems a little bit soiled, if your shoe has a crack in the leather,
Or if more than one patch attests to more than one mending!
Poverty's greatest curse, much worse than the fact of it, is that
It makes men objects of mirth, ridiculed, humbled, embarrassed.
'Out of the front-row seats!' they cry when you're out of money,
Yield your place to the sons of some pimp, the spawn of some cathouse,
Some slick auctioneer's brat, or the louts some trainer has fathered
Or the well-groomed boys whose sire is a gladiator.   150
Such is the law of place, decreed by the nitwitted Otho:[8]
All the best seats are reserved for the classes who have the most
    money.
Who can marry a girl if he has less money than she does?
What poor man is an heir, or can hope to be? Which of them ever
Rates a political job, even the meanest and lowest?
Long before now, all poor Roman descendants of Romans
Ought to have marched out of town in one determined migration.
Men do not easily rise whose poverty hinders their merit.
Here it is harder than anywhere else: the lodgings are hovels,
Rents out of sight; your slaves take plenty to fill up their bellies   160
While you make do with a snack. You're ashamed of your earthenware
    dishes—
Ah, but that wouldn't be true if you lived content in the country,

---

8 A Roman emperor.

Wearing a dark-blue cape, and the hood thrown back on your
  shoulders.

"In a great part of this land of Italy, might as well face it,
No one puts on a toga unless he is dead. On festival days
Where the theater rises, cut from green turf, and with great pomp
Old familiar plays are staged again, and a baby,
Safe in his mother's lap, is scared of the grotesque mask,
There you see all dressed alike, the balcony and the front rows,
Even His Honor content with a tunic of simple white.   170
Here, beyond our means, we have to be smart, and too often
Get our effects with too much, an elaborate wardrobe, on credit!
This is a common vice; we must keep up with the neighbors,
Poor as we are. I tell you, everything here costs you something.
How much to give Cossus the time of day, or receive from Veiento
One quick glance, with his mouth buttoned up for fear he might greet
    you?
One shaves his beard, another cuts off the locks of his boy friend,
Offerings fill the house, but these, you find, you will pay for.
Put this in your pipe and smoke it—we have to pay tribute
Giving the slaves a bribe for the prospect of bribing their masters.   180

"Who, in Praeneste's cool, or the wooded Volsinian uplands,
Who, on Tivoli's heights, or a small town like Gabii, say,
Fears the collapse of his house? But Rome is supported on pipestems,
Matchsticks; it's cheaper, so, for the landlord to shore up his ruins,
Patch up the old cracked walls, and notify all the tenants
They can sleep secure, though the beams are in ruins above them.
No, the place to live is out there, where no cry of *Fire!*
Sounds the alarm of the night, with a neighbor yelling for water,
Moving his chattels and goods, and the whole third story is smoking.
This you'll never know: for if the ground is scared first,   190
You are the last to burn, up there where the eaves of the attic
Keep off the rain, and the doves are brooding over their nest eggs.
Codrus owned one bed, too small for a midget to sleep on,
Six little jugs he had, and a tankard adorning his sideboard,
Under whose marble (clay), a bust or a statute of Chiron,
Busted, lay on its side; an old locker held Greek books
Whose divinest lines were gnawed by the mice, those vandals.
Codrus had nothing, no doubt, and yet he succeeded, poor fellow,
Losing that nothing, his all. And this is the very last straw—

No one will help him out with a meal or lodging or shelter.　　200
Stripped to the bone, begging for crusts, he still receives nothing.

"Yet if Asturicus' mansion burns down, what a frenzy of sorrow!
Mothers dishevel themselves, the leaders dress up in black,
Courts are adjourned. We groan at the fall of the city, we hate
The fire, and the fire still burns, and while it is burning,
Somebody rushes up to replace the loss of the marble,
Some one chips in toward a building fund, another gives statues,
Naked and shining white, some masterpiece of Euphranor
Or Polyclitus' chef d'oeuvre; and here's a fellow with bronzes
Sacred to Asian gods. Books, chests, a bust of Minerva,　　210
A bushel of silver coins. *To him that hath shall be given!*
This Persian, childless, of course, the richest man in the smart set,
Now has better things, and more, than before the disaster.
How can we help but think he started the fire on purpose?

"Tear yourself from the games, and get a place in the country!
One little Latian town, like Sora, say, or Frusino,
Offers a choice of homes, at a price you pay here, in one year,
Renting some hole in the wall. Nice houses, too, with a garden,
Springs bubbling up from the grass, no need for a windlass or bucket,
Plenty to water your flowers, if they need it, without any trouble.　　220
Live there, fond of your hoe, an independent producer,
Willing and able to feed a hundred good vegetarians.
Isn't it something, to feel, wherever you are, how far off,
You are a monarch? At least, lord of a single lizard.

"Here in town the sick die from insomnia mostly.
Undigested food, on a stomach burning with ulcers,
Brings on listlessness, but who can sleep in a flophouse?
Who but the rich can afford sleep and a garden apartment?
That's the source of infection. The wheels creak by on the narrow
Streets of the wards, the drivers squabble and brawl when they're
　　stopped,　　230
More than enough to frustrate the drowsiest son of a sea cow.
When his business calls, the crowd makes way, as the rich man,
Carried high in his car, rides over them, reading or writing,
Even taking a snooze, perhaps, for the motion's composing.
Still, he gets where he wants before we do; for all of our hurry
Traffic gets in our way, in front, around and behind us.

Somebody gives me a shove with an elbow, or two-by-four scantling.
One clunks my head with a beam, another cracks down with a beer
    keg.
Mud is thick on my shins, I am trampled by somebody's big feet.
Now what?—a soldier grinds his hobnails into my toes.   240

"Don't you see the mob rushing along to the handout?
There are a hundred guests, each one with his kitchen servant.
Even Samson himself could hardly carry those burdens,
Pots and pans some poor little slave tries to keep on his head, while
    he hurries
Hoping to keep the fire alive by the wind of his running.
Tunics, new-darned, are ripped to shreds; there's the flash of a fir
    beam
Huge on some great dray, and another carries a pine tree,
Nodding above our heads and threatening death to the people.
What will be left of the mob, if that cart of Ligurian marble
Breaks its axle down and dumps its load on these swarms?   250
Who will identify limbs or bones? The poor man's cadaver,
Crushed, disappears like his breath. And meanwhile, at home, his
    household
Washes the dishes, and puffs up the fire, with all kinds of a clatter
Over the smeared flesh-scrapers, the flasks of oil, and the towels.
So the boys rush around, while their late master is sitting,
Newly come to the bank of the Styx, afraid of the filthy
Ferryman there, since he has no fare, not even a copper
In his dead mouth to pay for the ride through that muddy whirlpool.

"Look at other things, the various dangers of nighttime.
How high it is to the cornice that breaks, and a chunk beats my
    brains out,   260
Or some slob heaves a jar, broken or cracked, from a window.
Bang! It comes down with a crash and proves its weight on the side-
    walk.
You are a thoughtless fool, unmindful of sudden disaster,
If you don't make your will before you go out to have dinner.
There are as many deaths in the night as there are open windows
Where you pass by; if you're wise, you will pray, in your wretched
    devotions,
People may be content with no more than emptying slop jars.

"There your hell-raising drunk, who has had the bad luck to kill no
    one,
Tosses in restless rage, like Achilles mourning Patroclus,
Turns from his face to his back, can't sleep, for only a fracas   270
Gives him the proper sedation. But any of these young hoodlums,
All steamed up on wine, watches his step when the crimson
Cloak goes by, a lord, with a long, long line of attendants,
Torches and brazen lamps, warning him, *Keep your distance!*
Me, however, whose torch is the moon, or the feeblest candle
Fed by a sputtering wick, he absolutely despises.
Here is how it all starts, the fight, if you think it is fighting
When he throws all the punches, and all I do is absorb them.
He stops. He tells me to stop. I stop. I have to obey him.
What can you do when he's mad and bigger and stronger than you
    are?   280
'Where do you come from?' he cries, 'you wino, you bean-bloated
    bastard?
Off what shoemaker's dish have you fed on chopped leeks and boiled
    lamb-lip?
What? No answer? Speak up, or take a swift kick in the rear.
Tell me where you hang out—in some praying-house with Jewboys?'
If you try to talk back, or sneak away without speaking,
All the same thing: you're assaulted, and then put under a bail bond
For committing assault. This is a poor man's freedom.
Beaten, cut up by fists, he begs and implores his assailant,
Please, for a chance to go home with a few teeth left in his mouth.

"This is not all you must fear. Shut up your house or your store,   290
Bolts and padlocks and bars will never keep out all the burglars,
Or a holdup man will do you in with a switch blade.
If the guards are strong over Pontine marshes and pinewoods
Near Volturno, the scum of the swamps and the filth of the forest
Swirl into Rome, the great sewer, their sanctuary, their haven.
Furnaces blast and anvils groan with the chains we are forging:
What other use have we for iron and steel? There is danger
We will have little left for hoes and mattocks and ploughshares.
Happy the men of old, those primitive generations
Under the tribunes and kings, when Rome had only one jailhouse!   300

"There is more I could say, I could give you more of my reasons,
But the sun slants down, my oxen seem to be calling,

My man with the whip is impatient, I must be on my way.
So long! Don't forget me. Whenever you come to Aquino
Seeking relief from Rome, send for me. I'll come over
From my bay to your hills, hiking along in my thick boots
Toward your chilly fields. What's more, I promise to listen
If your satirical verse esteems me worthy the honor."

Questions for Discussion

1. What is the importance of the setting for this incident?

2. What are the chief complaints which Umbricius makes against Rome?

3. Why does Umbricius think he will be happier at Cumae?

4. Why does Umbricius seem to have failed in Rome?

5. What are the criticisms that Umbricius makes of the foreigners, especially the Greeks? Is his prejudice merely personal?

6. How does the passage in lines 171-178 figure in the criticism of urban extravagance?

7. Is Umbricius a plain, simple man? Does the manner of his speech seem consistent with his character?

8. Compare Juvenal's satiric treatment of Rome with Horace's.

William Shakespeare (1564-1616)

Sonnet 130

My mistress' eyes are nothing like the sun;
Coral is far more red than her lips' red;
If snow be white, why then her breasts are dun;
If hairs be wires, black wires grow on her head.
I have seen roses damasked,[1] red and white,
But no such roses see I in her cheeks;
And in some perfumes is there more delight
Than in the breath that from my mistress reeks.
I love to hear her speak, yet well I know
That music hath a far more pleasing sound;
I grant I never saw a goddess go,[2]
My mistress, when she walks, treads on the ground.
And yet, by heaven, I think my love as rare
As any she belied with false compare.

Questions for Discussion

1. This is an anti-Petrarchan sonnet written to satirize the exaggerated praise of a woman the Italian poet Petrarch made famous. What is the picture of this ideal beauty that Shakespeare is mocking?

2. How is the woman Shakespeare praises the opposite in every way from the woman he is making fun of? Is she lacking in beauty altogether?

3. Is there any reason for presenting the description of the lady in the precise way it is done, beginning with her eyes and ending with her walk?

4. Is the couplet at the end of the sonnet repetitious or does it contribute in a meaningful way to the main theme of the poem?

---

[1] Variegated.
[2] Walk.

John Donne (1572-1631)

Song

Go and catch a falling star,
  Get with child a mandrake root,[1]
Tell me where all past years are,
  Or who cleft the Devil's foot,
Teach me to hear mermaids singing,
Or to keep off envy's stinging,
      And find
      What wind
Serves to advance an honest mind.

If thou beest born to strange sights,
  Things invisible to see,
Ride ten thousand days and nights,
  Till age snow white hairs on thee,
Thou, when thou return'st, wilt tell me
All strange wonders that befell thee,
      And swear
      Nowhere
Lives a woman true, and fair.

If thou find'st one, let me know,
  Such a pilgrimage were sweet;
Yet do not, I would not go,
  Though at next door we might meet;
Though she were true when you met her,
And last till you write your letter,
      Yet she
      Will be
False, ere I come, to two, or three.

---

[1] The forked root of the mandrake resembling the lower part of the human body. Of course getting such a root with child is an impossibility.

Questions for Discussion

1. What aspect of womanhood is Donne satirizing in this poem?

2. What do all the images in the first stanza have in common? How are such images related to the kind of woman Donne is satirizing?

3. To whom is Donne addressing the poem? Characterize this person as well as the speaker.

4. Explain how the argument is developed in the poem.

5. Contrast this anti-Petrarchan poem with Shakespeare's. Which one do you think satirizes more effectively a conventional way of writing love poetry?

Jean de La Fontaine (1621-1695)

The Animals and the Plague

From *Fables*

TRANSLATED BY SIR EDWARD MARSH

Of old that fearful visitation
Which Heav'n in righteous indignation
Sends on the earth t' avenge its outraged law,
The Plague (for I must write the hideous word),
Which in one day can glut black Pluto's maw,
Made onset upon beast and bird.
Though all died not, yet all were smitten; none
Was left with strength to carry on
The business of a life so near to death:
No cate[1] their appetite could move:　　　　　　　　　10
The wolves, the foxes, wanted breath
To track their gentle prey: dove fled from dove:
Love was no more, and joy outlived not love.

　　King Lion called a Council. "Friends," said he,
" 'Tis plain this agony must be
God's punishment for some portentous crime.
'Tis therefore meet the guiltiest should fall
A sacrifice t' appease that wrath sublime,
And thus, maybe, obtain new health for all.
History teaches us that many a crises　　　　　　　　20
Has been resolved by suchlike sacrifices.
Let us then lay aside our vanities,
And frankly probe our consciences.

"The Animals and the Plague" from *The Fables of La Fontaine*, translated by Edward Marsh. Copyright 1925 by Harper & Brothers; renewed 1953 by Sir Edward Marsh. Reprinted by permission of Harper & Row, Publishers.
[1] Choice food, delicacy.

28

As for Myself, I fear I am a glutton,
And many a harmless sheep has been my mutton.
Indeed, 'tis not unknown for me to chew
The shepherd too!
I'm ready, then, if I'm the guilty one;
But first let each confess as I have done;
For 'tis but just to wish the doom should fall   30
Upon the chiefest criminal."

    "Sire," cried the Fox, "a King can be too good!
Such scruples show too delicate a nature!
Why, what's a sheep—that dull, plebeian creature?
Is it a sin to use her flesh for food?
Nay, 'twas an honour for the trash
To make Your Majesty a hash.
As for the shepherd, plainly he
Deserved the utmost penalty,
As one of those who on our ill-used races   40
Usurp a power which has no rational basis."

    The Fox sat down amid prolonged applause,
'Twas felt that it would be unwise
Too rigidly to scrutinize
What Tiger, Bear, and other dignit'ries
Had done in violation of the laws;
And all the quarrelsome folk with teeth and claws,
Down to the Dog, were lauded to the skies.

    All of these disposed of, came the Ass.
"Once, long ago, I recollect," said he,   50
"Pacing the meadows of a monast'ry.
Hunger, the chance, the freshness of the grass,
And I suppose the Devil, tempted me
To crop some blades, enough to cool my tongue;
Though, truth to tell, I knew that it was wrong."

    Thereat arose an angry hum.
A Wolf, who had some skill in legal patter,
Proved 'twas from this vile wretch, this mangy scum,
That all their ills and tribulation came.

His peddling fault was judged a hanging matter.   60
What, eat your neighbour's grass? Oh, sin and shame!
Nothing but death could expiate
So foul a deed. He hadn't long to wait.

At Court, the diff'rence between right and wrong
Depends on whether you are weak or strong.

Questions for Discussion

1. Does La Fontaine have the animals speak in character?

2. Where does the Lion wish the blame for the plague to lie?

3. Discuss the irony in the remark which the Fox makes about shepherds.

4. Is legal injustice the point of La Fontaine's satire?

Molière (1622-1673)

The Misanthrope

ENGLISH VERSION BY RICHARD WILBUR

CHARACTERS

ALCESTE, in love with Célimène
PHILINTE, Alceste's friend
ORONTE, in love with Célimène
CÉLIMÈNE, Alceste's beloved
ELIANTE, Célimène's cousin
ARSINOÉ, a friend of Célimène's
ACASTE } Marquesses
CLITANDRE
BASQUE, Célimène's servant
A GUARD of the Marshalsea
DUBOIS, Alceste's valet

The Scene throughout is in Célimène's house at Paris.

31

ACT I

SCENE 1. (PHILINTE, ALCESTE)

PHILINTE. Now, what's got into you?
ALCESTE (seated).   Kindly leave me alone.
PHILINTE. Come, come, what is it? This lugubrious tone . . .
ALCESTE. Leave me, I said; you spoil my solitude.
PHILINTE. Oh, listen to me, now, and don't be rude.
ALCESTE. I choose to be rude, Sir, and to be hard of hearing.
PHILINTE. These ugly moods of yours are not endearing;
    Friends though we are, I really must insist . . .
ALCESTE (*abruptly rising*). Friends? Friends, you say? Well, cross me
    off your list.
    I've been your friend till now, as you well know;
    But after what I saw a moment ago   10
    I tell you flatly that our ways must part.
    I wish no place in a dishonest heart.
PHILINTE. Why, what have I done, Alceste? Is this quite just?
ALCESTE. My God, you ought to die of self-disgust.
    I call your conduct inexcusable, Sir,
    And every man of honor will concur.
    I see you almost hug a man to death,
    Exclaim for joy until you're out of breath,
    And supplement these loving demonstrations
    With endless offers, vows, and protestations;   20
    Then when I ask you "Who was that?" I find
    That you can barely bring his name to mind!
    Once the man's back is turned, you cease to love him,
    And speak with absolute indifference of him!
    By God, I say it's base and scandalous
    To falsify the heart's affections thus;
    If I caught myself behaving in such a way,
    I'd hang myself for shame, without delay.
PHILINTE. It hardly seems a hanging matter to me;
    I hope that you will take it graciously   30
    If I extend myself a slight reprieve,
    And live a little longer, by your leave.
ALCESTE. How dare you joke about a crime so grave?
PHILINTE. What crime? How else are people to behave?

ALCESTE. I'd have them be sincere, and never part
   With any word that isn't from the heart.
PHILINTE. When someone greets us with a show of pleasure,
   It's but polite to give him equal measure,
   Return his love the best that we know how,
   And trade him offer for offer, vow for vow.   40
ALCESTE. No, no, this formula you'd have me follow,
   However fashionable, is false and hollow,
   And I despise the frenzied operations
   Of all these barterers of protestations,
   These lavishers of meaningless embraces,
   These utterers of obliging commonplaces,
   Who court and flatter everyone on earth
   And praise the fool no less than the man of worth.
   Should you rejoice that someone fondles you,
   Offers his love and service, swears to be true,   50
   And fills your ears with praises of your name,
   When to the first damned fop he'll say the same?
   No, no: no self-respecting heart would dream
   Of prizing so promiscuous an esteem;
   However high the praise, there's nothing worse
   Than sharing honors with the universe.
   Esteem is founded on comparison:
   To honor all men is to honor none.
   Since you embrace this indiscriminate vice,
   Your friendship comes at far too cheap a price;   60
   I spurn the easy tribute of a heart
   Which will not set the worthy man apart:
   I choose, Sir, to be chosen; and in fine,
   The friend of mankind is no friend of mine.
PHILINTE. But in polite society, custom decrees
   That we show certain outward coutesies. . . .
ALCESTE. Ah, no! we should condemn with all our force
   Such false and artificial intercourse.
   Let men behave like men; let them display
   Their inmost hearts in everything they say;   70
   Let the heart speak, and let our sentiments
   Not mask themselves in silly compliments.
PHILINTE. In certain cases it would be uncouth
   And most absurd to speak the naked truth;
   With all respect for your exalted notions,
   It's often best to veil one's true emotions.

Wouldn't the social fabric come undone
If we were wholly frank with everyone?
Suppose you met with someone you couldn't bear;
Would you inform him of it then and there?   80

ALCESTE. Yes.

PHILINTE.   Then you'd tell old Emilie it's pathetic
The way she daubs her features with cosmetic
And plays the gay coquette at sixty-four?

ALCESTE. I would.

PHILINTE.   And you'd call Dorilas a bore,
And tell him every ear at court is lame
From hearing him brag about his noble name?

ALCESTE. Precisely.

PHILINTE.   Ah, you're joking.

ALCESTE.   *Au contraire:*
In this regard there's none I'd choose to spare.
All are corrupt; there's nothing to be seen
In court or town but aggravates my spleen.   90
I fall into deep gloom and melancholy
When I survey the scene of human folly,
Finding on every hand base flattery,
Injustice, fraud, self-interest, treachery. . . .
Ah, it's too much; mankind has grown so base,
I mean to break with the whole human race.

PHILINTE. This philosophic rage is a bit extreme;
You've no idea how comical you seem;
Indeed, we're like those brothers in the play
Called *School for Husbands*, one of whom was prey . . .   100

ALCESTE. Enough, now! None of your stupid similes.

PHILINTE. Then let's have no more tirades, if you please.
The world won't change, whatever you say or do;
And since plain speaking means so much to you,
I'll tell you plainly that by being frank
You've earned the reputation of a crank,
And that you're thought ridiculous when you rage
And rant against the manners of the age.

ALCESTE. So much the better; just what I wish to hear.
No news could be more grateful to my ear.   110
All men are so destestable in my eyes,
I should be sorry if they thought me wise.

PHILINTE. Your hatred's very sweeping, is it not?

ALCESTE. Quite right: I hate the whole degraded lot.

PHILINTE. Must all poor human creatures be embraced,
    Without distinction, by your vast distaste?
    Even in these bad times, there are surely a few . . .
ALCESTE. No, I include all men in one dim view:
    Some men I hate for being rogues: the others
    I hate because they treat the rogues like brothers,   120
    And, lacking a virtuous scorn for what is vile,
    Receive the villain with a complaisant smile,
    Notice how tolerant people choose to be
    Toward that bold rascal who's at law with me.
    His social polish can't conceal his nature;
    One sees at once that he's a treacherous creature;
    No one could possibly be taken in
    By those soft speeches and that sugary grin.
    The whole world knows the shady means by which
    The low-brow's grown so powerful and rich,   130
    And risen to a rank so bright and high
    That virtue can but blush, and merit sigh.
    Whenever his name comes up in conversation,
    None will defend his wretched reputation;
    Call him knave, liar, scoundrel, and all the rest,
    Each head will nod, and no one will protest.
    And yet his smirk is seen in every house,
    He's greeted everywhere with smiles and bows,
    And when there's any honor that can be got
    By pulling strings, he'll get it, like as not.   140
    My God! It chills my heart to see the ways
    Men come to terms with evil nowadays;
    Sometimes, I swear, I'm moved to flee and find
    Some desert land unfouled by humankind.
PHILINTE. Come, let's forget the follies of the times
    And pardon mankind for its petty crimes;
    Let's have an end of rantings and of railings,
    And show some leniency toward human failings.
    This world requires a pliant rectitude;
    Too stern a virtue makes one stiff and rude;   150
    Good sense views all extremes with detestation,
    And bids us to be noble in moderation.
    The rigid virtues of the ancient days
    Are not for us; they jar with all our ways
    And ask of us too lofty a perfection.
    Wise men accept their times without objection,

And there's no greater folly, if you ask me,
Than trying to reform society.
Like you, I see each day a hundred and one
Unhandsome deeds that might be better done,   160
But still, for all the faults that meet my view,
I'm never known to storm and rave like you.
I take men as they are, or let them be,
And teach my soul to bear their frailty;
And whether in court or town, whatever the scene,
My phlegm's as philosophic as your spleen.
ALCESTE. This phlegm which you so eloquently commend,
Does nothing ever rile it up, my friend?
Suppose some man you trust should treacherously
Conspire to rob you of your property,   170
And do his best to wreck your reputation?
Wouldn't you feel a certain indignation?
PHILINTE. Why, no. These faults of which you so complain
Are part of human nature, I maintain,
And it's no more a matter for disgust
That men are knavish, selfish and unjust,
Than that the vulture dines upon the dead,
And wolves are furious, and apes ill-bred.
ALCESTE. Shall I see myself betrayed, robbed, torn to bits,
And not . . . Oh, let's be still and rest our wits.   180
Enough of reasoning, now. I've had my fill.
PHILINTE. Indeed, you would do well, Sir, to be still.
Rage less at your opponent, and give some thought
To how you'll win this lawsuit that he's brought.
ALCESTE. I assure you I'll do nothing of the sort.
PHILINTE. Then who will plead your case before the court?
ALCESTE. Reason and right and justice will plead for me.
PHILINTE. Oh, Lord. What judges do you plan to see?
ALCESTE. Why, none. The justice of my cause is clear.
PHILINTE. Of course, man; but there's politics to fear. . . . 190
ALCESTE. No, I refuse to lift a hand. That's flat.
I'm either right, or wrong.
PHILINTE.   Don't count on that.
ALCESTE. No, I'll do nothing.
PHILINTE.   Your enemy's influence
Is great, you know . . .
ALCESTE.   That makes no difference.
PHILINTE. It will; you'll see.

ALCESTE.   Must honor bow to guile?
  If so, I shall be proud to lose the trial.
PHILINTE. Oh, really . . .
ALCESTE.   I'll discover by this case
  Whether or not men are sufficiently base
  And impudent and villainous and perverse
  To do me wrong before the universe.   200
PHILINTE. What a man!
ALCESTE.   Oh, I could wish, whatever the cost,
  Just for the beauty of it, that my trial were lost.
PHILINTE. If people heard you talking so, Alceste,
  They'd split their sides. Your name would be a jest.
ALCESTE. So much the worse for jesters.
PHILINTE.   May I enquire
  Whether this rectitude you so admire,
  And these hard virtues you're enamored of
  Are qualities of the lady whom you love?
  It much surprises me that you, who seem
  To view mankind with furious disesteem,   210
  Have yet found something to enchant your eyes
  Amidst a species which you so despise.
  And what is more amazing, I'm afraid,
  Is the most curious choice your heart has made.
  The honest Éliante is fond of you,
  Arsinoé, the prude, admires you too;
  And yet your spirit's been perversely led
  To choose the flighty Célimène instead,
  Whose brittle malice and coquettish ways
  So typify the manners of our days.   220
  How is it that the traits you most abhor
  Are bearable in this lady you adore?
  Are you so blind with love that you can't find them?
  Or do you contrive, in her case, not to mind them?
ALCESTE. My love for that young widow's not the kind
  That can't perceive defects; no, I'm not blind.
  I see her faults, despite my ardent love,
  And all I see I fervently reprove.
  And yet I'm weak; for all her falsity,
  That woman knows the art of pleasing me,   230
  And though I never cease complaining of her,
  I swear I cannot manage not to love her.
  Her charm outweighs her faults; I can but aim

To cleanse her spirit in my love's pure flame.

PHILINTE. That's no small task; I wish you all success.
  You think then that she loves you?

ALCESTE.   Heavens, yes!
  I wouldn't love her did she not love me.

PHILINTE. Well, if her taste for you is plain to see,
  Why do these rivals cause you such despair?

ALCESTE. True love, Sir, is possessive, and cannot bear   240
  To share with all the world. I'm here today
  To tell her she must send that mob away.

PHILINTE. If I were you, and had your choice to make,
  Éliante, her cousin, would be the one I'd take;
  That honest heart, which cares for you alone,
  Would harmonize far better with your own.

ALCESTE. True, true: each day my reason tells me so;
  But reason doesn't rule in love, you know.

PHILINTE. I fear some bitter sorrow is in store;
  This love . . .   250

SCENE 2. (ORONTE, ALCESTE, PHILINTE)

ORONTE (*to Alceste*). The servants told me at the door
  That Éliante and Célimène were out,
  But when I heard, dear Sir, that you were about,
  I came to say, without exaggeration,
  That I hold you in the vastest admiration,
  And that it's always been my dearest desire
  To be the friend of one I so admire.
  I hope to see my love of merit requited,
  And you and I in friendship's bond united.
  I'm sure you won't refuse—if I may be frank—   10
  A friend of my devotedness—and rank.

(*During this speech of* ORONTE'S, ALCESTE *is abstracted, and seems
unaware that he is being spoken to. He only breaks off his reverie
when* ORONTE *says:*)

It was for you, if you please, that my words were intended.

ALCESTE. For me, Sir?

ORONTE.   Yes, for you. You're not offended?

ALCESTE. By no means. But this much surprises me. . . .

The honor comes most unexpectedly. . . .
ORONTE. My high regard should not astonish you;
　　The whole world feels the same. It is your due.
ALCESTE. Sir . . .
ORONTE.　　　Why, in all the State there isn't one
　　Can match your merits; they shine, Sir, like the sun.
ALCESTE. Sir . . .
ORONTE.　　　You are higher in my estimation　　　　20
　　Than all that's most illustrious in the nation.
ALCESTE. Sir . . .
ORONTE.　　　If I lie, may heaven strike me dead!
　　To show you that I mean what I have said,
　　Permit me, Sir, to embrace you most sincerely,
　　And swear that I will prize our friendship dearly.
　　Give me your hand. And now, Sir, if you choose,
　　We'll make our vows.
ALCESTE.　　　　　　Sir . . .
ORONTE.　　　　　　　　　　What! You refuse?
ALCESTE. Sir, it's a very great honor you extend:
　　But friendship is a sacred thing, my friend;
　　It would be profanation to bestow　　　　　　30
　　The name of friend on one you hardly know.
　　All parts are better played when well-rehearsed;
　　Let's put off friendship, and get acquainted first.
　　We may discover it would be unwise
　　To try to make our natures harmonize.
ORONTE. By heaven! You're sagacious to the core;
　　This speech has made me admire you even more.
　　Let time, then, bring us closer day by day;
　　Meanwhile, I shall be yours in every way.
　　If, for example, there should be anything　　　　40
　　You wish at court, I'll mention it to the King.
　　I have his ear, of course; it's quite well known
　　That I am much in favor with the throne.
　　In short, I am your servant. And now, dear friend,
　　Since you have such fine judgment, I intend
　　To please you, if I can, with a small sonnet
　　I wrote not long ago. Please comment on it,
　　And tell me whether I ought to publish it.
ALCESTE. You must excuse me, Sir; I'm hardly fit
　　To judge such matters.
ORONTE.　　　　　　　　Why not?

ALCESTE. I am, I fear, 50
Inclined to be unfashionably sincere.
ORONTE. Just what I ask; I'd take no satisfaction
In anything but your sincere reaction.
I beg you not to dream of being kind.
ALCESTE. Since you desire it, Sir, I'll speak my mind.
ORONTE. *Sonnet.* It's a sonnet. . . . *Hope* . . . The poem's addressed
To a lady who wakened hopes within my breast.
Hope . . . this is not the pompous sort of thing,
Just modest little verses, with a tender ring.
ALCESTE. Well, we shall see.
ORONTE. *Hope* . . . I'm anxious to hear 60
Whether the style seems properly smooth and clear,
And whether the choice of words is good or bad.
ALCESTE. We'll see, we'll see.
ORONTE. Perhaps I ought to add
That it took me only a quarter-hour to write it,
ALCESTE. The time's irrelevant, Sir: kindly recite it.
ORONTE (*reading*). *Hope comforts us awhile, 'tis true,*
Lulling our cares with careless laughter,
And yet such joy is full of rue,
My Phyllis, if nothing follows after.
PHILINTE. I'm charmed by this already; the style's delightful. 70
ALCESTE (*sotto voce, to Philinte*). How can you say that? Why, the thing
is frightful.
ORONTE. *Your fair face smiled on me awhile,*
But was it kindness so to enchant me?
'Twould have been fairer not to smile,
If hope was all you meant to grant me.
PHILINTE. What a clever thought! How handsomely you phrase it!
ALCESTE (*sotto voce, to Philinte*). You know the thing is trash.
How dare you praise it?
ORONTE. *If it's to be my passion's fate*
Thus everlastingly to wait, 80
Then death will come to set me free:
For death is fairer than the fair;
Phyllis, to hope is to despair
When one must hope eternally.
PHILINTE. The close is exquisite—full of feeling and grace.
ALCESTE (*sotto voce, aside*). Oh, blast the close; you'd better close your
face
Before you send your lying soul to hell.

PHILINTE. I can't remember a poem I've liked so well.

ALCESTE (*sotto voce, aside*). Good Lord!

ORONTO (*to Philinte*).   I fear you're flattering me

    a bit.

PHILINTE. Oh, no!

ALCESTE (*sotto voce, aside*). What else d'you call it, you hypocrite?   90

ORONTE (*to Alceste*). But you, Sir, keep your promise now: don't shrink

   From telling me sincerely what you think.

ALCESTE. Sir, these are delicate matters; we all desire

   To be told that we've the true poetic fire.

   But once, to one whose name I shall not mention,

   I said, regarding some verse of his invention,

   That gentleman should rigorously control

   That itch to write which often afflicts the soul;

   That one should curb the heady inclination

   To publicize one's little avocation;   100

   And that in showing off one's works of art

   One often plays a very clownish part.

ORONTE. Are you suggesting in a devious way

   That I ought not . . .

ALCESTE.   Oh, that I do not say.

   Further, I told him that no fault is worse

   Than that of writing frigid, lifeless verse,

   And that the merest whisper of such a shame

   Suffices to destroy a man's good name.

ORONTE. D'you mean to say my sonnet's dull and trite?

ALCESTE. I don't say that. But I went on to cite   110

   Numerous cases of once-respected men

   Who came to grief by taking up the pen.

ORONTE. And am I like them? Do I write so poorly?

ALCESTE. I don't say that. But I told this person, "Surely

   You're under no necessity to compose;

   Why you should wish to publish, heaven knows.

   There's no excuse for printing tedious rot

   Unless one writes for bread, as you do not.

   Resist temptation, then, I beg of you;

   Conceal your pastimes from the public view;   120

   And don't give up, on any provocation,

   Your present high and courtly reputation,

   To purchase at a greedy printer's shop

   The name of silly author and scribbling fop."

   These were the points I tried to make him see.

ORONTE. I sense that they are also aimed at me;
But now—about my sonnet—I'd like to be told . . .
ALCESTE. Frankly, that sonnet should be pigeonholed.
You've chosen the worst models to imitate.
The style's unnatural. Let me illustrate: 130
   For example, *Your fair face smiled on me awhile,*
   Followed by, *'Twould have been fairer not to smile!*
   Or this: *such joy is full of rue;*
   Or this: *For death is fairer than the fair;*
   Or, *Phyllis, to hope is to despair*
    When one must hope eternally!
This artificial style, that's all the fashion,
Has neither taste, nor honesty, nor passion;
It's nothing but a sort of wordy play,
And nature never spoke in such a way.   140
What, in this shallow age, is not debased?
Our fathers, though less refined, had better taste;
I'd barter all that men admire today
For one old love song I shall try to say:
   If the King had given me for my own
   Paris, his citadel,
   And I for that must leave alone
   Her whom I love so well,
   I'd say then to the Crown,
   Take back your glittering town;   150
   My darling is more fair, I swear,
   My darling is more fair.
The rhyme's not rich, the style is rough and old,
But don't you see that it's the purest gold
Beside the tinsel nonsense now preferred,
And that there's passion in its every word?
   If the King had given me for my own
   Paris, his citadel,
   And I for that must leave alone
   Her whom I love so well,   160
   I'd say then to the Crown,
   Take back your glittering town;
   My darling is more fair, I swear,
   My darling is more fair.
There speaks a loving heart. (*To Philinte.*) You're laughing, eh?
Laugh on, my precious wit. Whatever you say,
I hold that song's worth all the bibelots

That people hail today with ah's and oh's.
ORONTE. And I maintain my sonnet's very good.
ALCESTE. It's not at all surprising that you should.　　　　　170
　　You have your reasons; permit me to have mine
　　For thinking that you cannot write a line.
ORONTE. Others have praised my sonnet to the skies.
ALCESTE. I lack their art of telling pleasant lies.
ORONTE. You seem to think you've got no end of wit.
ALCESTE. To praise your verse, I'd need still more of it.
ORONTE. I'm not in need of your approval, Sir.
ALCESTE. That's good; you couldn't have it if you were.
ORONTE. Come now, I'll lend you the subject of my sonnet;
　　I'd like to see you try to improve upon it.　　　　　180
ALCESTE. I might, by chance, write something just as shoddy;
　　But then I wouldn't show it to everybody.
ORONTE. You're most opinionated and conceited.
ALCESTE. Go find your flatterers, and be better treated.
ORONTE. Look here, my little fellow, pray watch your tone.
ALCESTE. My great big fellow, you'd better watch your own.
PHILINTE (*stepping between them*). Oh, please, please, gentlemen!
　　This will never do.
ORONTE. The fault is mine, and I leave the field to you.
　　I am your servant, Sir, in every way.　　　　　190
ALCESTE. And I, Sir, am your most abject valet.

SCENE 3. (PHILINTE, ALCESTE)

PHILINTE. Well, as you see, sincerity in excess
　　Can get you into a very pretty mess;
　　Oronte was hungry for appreciation. . . .
ALCESTE. Don't speak to me.
PHILINTE.　　　　　　　　What?
ALCESTE.　　　　　　　　　　　No more conversation.
PHILINTE. Really, now . . .
ALCESTE.　　　　　　　Leave me alone.
PHILINTE.　　　　　　　　　　　If I . . .
ALCESTE.　　　　　　　　　　　　　　Out of my sight!
PHILINTE. But what . . .
ALCESTE.　　　　　　I won't listen.
PHILINTE.　　　　　　　　　　But . . .
ALCESTE.　　　　　　　　　　　　Silence!

PHILINTE.   Now, is it polite . . .
ALCESTE. By heaven, I've had enough. Don't follow me.
PHILINTE. Ah, you're just joking. I'll keep you company.

ACT II

SCENE 1. (ALCESTE, CÉLIMÈNE)

ALCESTE. Shall I speak plainly, Madam? I confess
  Your conduct gives me infinite distress,
  And my resentment's grown too hot to smother.
  Soon, I foresee, we'll break with one another.
  If I said otherwise, I should deceive you;
  Sooner or later, I shall be forced to leave you,
  And if I swore that we shall never part,
  I should misread the omens of my heart.
CÉLIMÈNE. You kindly saw me home, it would appear,
  So as to pour invectives in my ear.   10
ALCESTE. I've no desire to quarrel. But I deplore
  Your inability to shut the door
  On all these suitors who beset you so.
  There's what annoys me, if you care to know.
CÉLIMÈNE. Is it my fault that all these men pursue me?
  Am I to blame if they're attracted to me?
  And when they gently beg an audience,
  Ought I to take a stick and drive them hence?
ALCESTE. Madam, there's no necessity for a stick;
  A less responsive heart would do the trick.   20
  Of your attractiveness I don't complain;
  But those your charms attract, you then detain
  By a most melting and receptive manner,
  And so enlist their hearts beneath your banner.
  It's the agreeable hopes which you excite
  That keep these lovers round you day and night;
  Were they less liberally smiled upon,
  That sighing troop would very soon be gone.
  But tell me, Madam, why it is that lately
  This man Clitandre interests you so greatly?   30
  Because of what high merits do you deem

Him worthy of the honor of your esteem?
Is it that your admiring glances linger
On the splendidly long nail of his little finger?
Or do you share the general deep respect
For the blond wig he chooses to affect?
Are you in love with his embroidered hose?
Do you adore his ribbons and his bows?
Or is it that this paragon bewitches
Your tasteful eye with his vast German breeches?   40
Perhaps his giggle, or his falsetto voice,
Makes him the latest gallant of your choice?
CÉLIMÈNE. You're much mistaken to resent him so.
Why I put up with him you surely know:
My lawsuit's very shortly to be tried,
And I must have his influence on my side.
ALCESTE. Then lose your lawsuit, Madam, or let it drop;
Don't torture me by humoring such a fop.
CÉLIMÈNE. You're jealous of the whole world, Sir.
ALCESTE.   That's true,
Since the whole world is well-received by you.   50
CÉLIMÈNE. That my good nature is so unconfined
Should serve to pacify your jealous mind;
Were I to smile on one, and scorn the rest,
Then you might have some cause to be distressed.
ALCESTE. Well, if I mustn't be jealous, tell me, then,
Just how I'm better treated than other men.
CÉLIMÈNE. You know you have my love. Will that not do?
ALCESTE. What proof have I that what you say is true?
CÉLIMÈNE. I would expect, Sir, that my having said it
Might give the statement sufficient credit.   60
ALCESTE. But how can I be sure that you don't tell
The selfsame thing to other men as well?
CÉLIMÈNE. What a gallant speech! How flattering to me!
What a sweet creature you make me out to be!
Well, then to save you from the pangs of doubt,
All that I've said I hereby cancel out;
Now, none but yourself shall make a monkey of you:
Are you content?
ALCESTE.   Why, why am I doomed to love you?
I swear that I shall bless the blissful hour
When this poor heart's no longer in your power!   70
I make no secret of it: I've done my best

To exorcise this passion from my breast;
But thus far all in vain; it will not go;
It's for my sins that I must love you so.
CÉLIMÈNE. Your love for me is matchless, Sir; that's clear.
ALCESTE. Indeed, in all the world it has no peer;
  Words can't describe the nature of my passion,
  And no man ever loved in such a fashion.
CÉLIMÈNE. Yes, it's a brand-new fashion, I agree:
  You show your love by castigating me,
  And all your speeches are enraged and rude.   80
  I've never been so furiously wooed.
ALCESTE. Yet you could calm that fury, if you chose.
  Come, shall we bring our quarrels to a close?
  Let's speak with open hearts, then, and begin . . .

SCENE 2. (CÉLIMÈNE, ALCESTE, BASQUE)

CÉLIMÈNE. What is it?
BASQUE.   Acaste is here.
CÉLIMÈNE.   Well, send him in.

SCENE 3. (CÉLIMÈNE, ALCESTE)

ALCESTE. What! Shall we never be alone at all?
  You're always ready to receive a call,
  And you can't bear, for ten ticks of the clock,
  Not to keep open house for all who knock.
CÉLIMÈNE. I couldn't refuse him: he'd be most put out.
ALCESTE. Surely that's not worth worrying about.
CÉLIMÈNE. Acaste would never forgive me if he guessed
  That I consider him a dreadful pest.
ALCESTE. If he's a pest, why bother with him then?
CÉLIMÈNE. Heavens! One can't antagonize such men;
  Why, they're the chartered gossips of the court,   10
  And have a say in things of every sort.
  One must receive them, and be full of charm;
  They're no great help, but they can do you harm,
  And though your influence be ever so great,
  They're hardly the best people to alienate.
ALCESTE. I see, dear lady, that you could make a case

For putting up with the whole human race;
These friendships that you calculate so nicely . . .

SCENE 4. (ALCESTE, CÉLIMÈNE, BASQUE)

BASQUE. Madam, Clitandre is here as well.
ALCESTE.   Precisely.
CÉLIMÈNE. Where are you going?
ALCESTE.   Elsewhere.
CÉLIMÈNE.   Stay.
ALCESTE.   No, no.
CÉLIMÈNE. Stay, Sir.
ALCESTE.   I can't.
CÉLIMÈNE.   I wish it.
ALCESTE.   No, I must go.
    I beg you, Madam, not to press the matter;
    You know I have no taste for idle chatter.
CÉLIMÈNE. Stay. I command you.
ALCESTE.   No, I cannot stay.
CÉLIMÈNE. Very well; you have my leave to go away.

SCENE 5. (ÉLIANTE, PHILINTE, ACASTE, CLITANDRE,
            ALCESTE, CÉLIMÈNE, BASQUE)

ÉLIANTE (*to Célimène*). The Marquesses have kindly come to call.
    Were they announced?
CÉLIMÈNE.   Yes, Basque, bring chairs for all.

(*Basque provides the chairs, and exits.*)

(*To Alceste.*) You haven't gone?
ALCESTE.   No; and I shan't depart
    Till you decide who's foremost in your heart.
CÉLIMÈNE. Oh, hush.
ALCESTE.   It's time to choose; take them, or me.
CÉLIMÈNE. You're mad.
ALCESTE.   I'm not, as you shall shortly see.
CÉLIMÈNE. Oh?
ALCESTE.   You'll decide.
CÉLIMÈNE.   You're joking now, dear friend.

ALCESTE. No, no; you'll choose; my patience is at an end.

CLITANDRE. Madam, I come from court, where poor Cléonte
　　Behaved like a perfect fool, as is his wont.　　　　　　　10
　　Has he no friend to counsel him, I wonder,
　　And teach him less unerringly to blunder?

CÉLIMÈNE. It's true, the man's a most accomplished dunce;
　　His gauche behavior charms the eye at once;
　　And every time one sees him, on my word,
　　His manner's grown a trifle more absurd.

ACASTE. Speaking of dunces, I've just now conversed
　　With old Damon, who's one of the very worst;
　　I stood a lifetime in the broiling sun
　　Before his dreary monologue was done.　　　　　　　　20

CÉLIMÈNE. Oh, he's a wondrous talker, and has the power
　　To tell you nothing hour after hour:
　　If, by mistake, he ever came to the point,
　　The shock would put his jawbone out of joint.

ÉLIANTE (*to Philinte*). The conversation takes its usual turn,
　　And all our dear friends' ears will shortly burn.

CLITANDRE. Timante's a character, Madam.

CÉLIMÈNE.　　　　　　　　　　　　　Isn't he, though?
　　A man of mystery from top to toe,
　　Who moves about in a romantic mist　　　　　　　　　30
　　On secret missions which do not exist.
　　His talk is full of eyebrows and grimaces;
　　How tired one gets of his momentous faces;
　　He's always whispering something confidential
　　Which turns out to be quite inconsequential;
　　Nothing's too slight for him to mystify;
　　He even whispers when he says "good-by."

ACASTE. Tell us about Géralde.

CÉLIMÈNE.　　　　　　　　　　That tiresome ass.
　　He mixes only with the titled class,
　　And fawns on dukes and princes, and is bored
　　With anyone who's not at least a lord.　　　　　　　　40
　　The man's obsessed with rank, and his discourses
　　Are all of hounds and carriages and horses;
　　He uses Christian names with all the great,
　　And the word Milord, with him, is out of date.

CLITANDRE. He's very taken with Bélise, I hear.

CÉLIMÈNE. She is the dreariest company, poor dear.
　　Whenever she comes to call, I grope about

To find some topic which will draw her out,
But, owing to her dry and faint replies,
The conversation wilts, and droops, and dies.   50
In vain one hopes to animate her face
By mentioning the ultimate commonplace;
But sun or shower, even hail or frost
Are matters she can instantly exhaust.
Meanwhile her visit, painful though it is,
Drags on and on through mute eternities,
And though you ask the time, and yawn, and yawn,
She sits there like a stone and won't be gone.
ACASTE. Now for Adraste.
CÉLIMÈNE.   Oh, that conceited elf
Has a gigantic passion for himself;   60
He rails against the court, and cannot bear it
That none will recognize his hidden merit;
All honors given to others give offense
To his imaginary excellence.
CLITANDRE. What about young Cléon? His house, they say,
Is full of the best society, night and day.
CÉLIMÈNE. His cook has made him popular, not he:
It's Cléon's table that people come to see.
ÉLIANTE. He gives a splendid dinner, you must admit.
CÉLIMÈNE. But must he serve himself along with it?   70
For my taste, he's a most insipid dish
Whose presence sours the wine and spoils the fish.
PHILINTE. Damis, his uncle, is admired no end.
What's your opinion, Madam?
CÉLIMÈNE.   Why, he's my friend.
PHILINTE. He seems a decent fellow, and rather clever.
CÉLIMÈNE. He works too hard at cleverness, however.
I hate to see him sweat and struggle so
To fill his conversation with bons mots.
Since he's decided to become a wit
His taste's so pure that nothing pleases it;   80
He scolds at all the latest books and plays,
Thinking that wit must never stoop to praise,
That finding fault's a sign of intellect,
That all appreciation is abject,
And that by damning everything in sight
One shows oneself in a distinguished light.
He's scornful even of our conversations:

Their trivial nature sorely tries his patience;
He folds his arms, and stands above the battle,
And listens sadly to our childish prattle.   90
ACASTE. Wonderful, Madam! You've hit him off precisely.
CLITANDRE. No one can sketch a character so nicely.
ALCESTE. How bravely, Sirs, you cut and thrust at all
   These absent fools, till one by one they fall:
   But let one come in sight, and you'll at once
   Embrace the man you lately called a dunce,
   Telling him in a tone sincere and fervent
   How proud you are to be his humble servant.
CLITANDRE. Why pick on us? *Madame's* been speaking, Sir.
   And you should quarrel, if you must, with her.   100
ALCESTE. No, no, by God, the fault is yours, because
   You lead her on with laughter and applause,
   And make her think that she's the more delightful
   The more her talk is scandalous and spiteful.
   Oh, she would stoop to malice far, far less
   If no such claque approved her cleverness.
   It's flatterers like you whose foolish praise
   Nourishes all the vices of these days.
PHILINTE. But why protest when someone ridicules
   Those you'd condemn, yourself, as knaves or fools?   110
CÉLIMÈNE. Why, Sir? Because he loves to make a fuss.
   You don't expect him to agree with us,
   When there's an opportunity to express
   His heaven-sent spirit of contrariness?
   What other people think, he can't abide;
   Whatever they say, he's on the other side;
   He lives in deadly terror of agreeing;
   'Twould make him seem an ordinary being.
   Indeed, he's so in love with contradiction,
   He'll turn against his most profound conviction   120
   And with a furious eloquence deplore it,
   If only someone else is speaking for it.
ALCESTE. Go on, dear lady, mock me as you please;
   You have your audience in ecstasies.
PHILINTE. But what she says is true: you have a way
   Of bridling at whatever people say;
   Whether they praise or blame, your angry spirit
   Is equally unsatisfied to hear it.
ALCESTE. Men, Sir, are always wrong, and that's the reason

That righteous anger's never out of season; 130
All that I hear in all their conversation
Is flattering praise or reckless condemnation.
CÉLIMÈNE. But . . .
ALCESTE.   No, no, Madam, I am forced to state
That you have pleasures which I deprecate,
And that these others, here, are much to blame
For nourishing the faults which are your shame.
CLITANDRE. I shan't defend myself, Sir; but I vow
I'd thought this lady faultless until now.
ACASTE. I see her charms and graces, which are many;
But as for faults, I've never noticed any. 140
ALCESTE. I see them, Sir; and rather than ignore them,
I strenuously criticize her for them.
The more one loves, the more one should object
To every blemish, every least defect.
Were I this lady, I would soon get rid
Of lovers who approved of all I did,
And by their slack indulgence and applause
Endorsed my follies and excused my flaws.
CÉLIMÈNE. If all heart beat according to your measure,
The dawn of love would be the end of pleasure; 150
And love would find its perfect consummation
In ecstasies of rage and reprobation.
ÉLIANTE. Love, as a rule, affects men otherwise,
And lovers rarely love to criticize.
They see their lady as a charming blur,
And find all things commendable in her.
If she has any blemish, fault, or shame,
They will redeem it by a pleasing name.
The pale-faced lady's lily-white, perforce;
The swarthy one's a sweet brunette, of course; 160
The spindly lady has a slender grace;
The fat one has a most majestic pace;
The plain one, with her dress in disarray,
They classify as *beauté négligée;*
The hulking one's a goddess in their eyes,
The dwarf, a concentrate of Paradise;
The haughty lady has a noble mind;
The mean one's witty, and the dull one's kind;
The chatterbox has liveliness and verve,
The mute one has a virtuous reserve. 170

So lovers manage, in their passion's cause,
To love their ladies even for their flaws.

ALCESTE. But I still say . . .

CÉLIMÉNE.   I think it would be nice
To stroll around the gallery once or twice.
What! You're not going, Sirs?

CLITANDRE AND ACASTE.   No, Madam, no.

ALCESTE. You seem to be in terror lest they go.
Do what you will, Sirs; leave, or linger on,
But I shan't go till after you are gone.

ACASTE. I'm free to linger, unless I should perceive
Madame is tired, and wishes me to leave.   180

CLITANDRE. And as for me, I needn't go today
Until the hour of the King's *coucher.*

CÉLIMÈNE (*to Alceste*). You're joking, surely?

ALCESTE.   Not in the least; we'll see
Whether you'd rather part with them, or me.

SCENE 6. (ALCESTE, CÉLIMÈNE, ÉLIANTE, ACASTE,
PHILINTE, CLITANDRE, BASQUE)

BASQUE (*to Alceste*). Sir, there's a fellow here who bids me state
That he must see you, and that it can't wait.

ALCESTE. Tell him that I have no such pressing affairs.

BASQUE. It's a long tailcoat that this fellow wears,
With gold all over.

CÉLIMÈNE (*to Alceste*). You'd best go down and see.
Or—have him enter.

SCENE 7. (ALCESTE, CÉLIMÈNE, ÉLIANTE, ACASTE,
PHILINTE, CLITANDRE, GUARD)

ALCESTE (*confronting the Guard*). Well, what do you want with me?
Come in, Sir.

GUARD.   I've a word, Sir, for your ear.

ALCESTE. Speak it aloud, Sir; I shall strive to hear.

GUARD. The Marshals have instructed me to say
You must report to them without delay.

ALCESTE. Who? Me, Sir?

GUARD.   Yes, Sir; you.

ALCESTE.   But what do they want?

PHILINTE *(to Alceste)*. To scotch your silly quarrel with Oronte.

CÉLIMÈNE *(to Philinte)*. What quarrel?

PHILINTE.   Oronte and he have fallen out
 Over some verse he spoke his mind about;
 The Marshals wish to arbitrate the matter.   1G

ALCESTE. Never shall I equivocate or flatter!

PHILINTE. You'd best obey their summons; come, let's go.

ALCESTE. How can they mend our quarrel, I'd like to know?
 Am I to make a cowardly retraction,
 And praise those jingles to his satisfaction?
 I'll not recant; I've judged that sonnet rightly.
 It's bad.

PHILINTE. But you might say so more politely. . . .

ALCESTE. I'll not back down; his verses make me sick.

PHILINTE. If only you could be more politic!   20
 But come, let's go.

ALCESTE.   I'll go, I won't unsay
 A single word.

PHILINTE.   Well, let's be on our way.

ALCESTE. Till I am ordered by my lord the King
 To praise that poem, I shall say the thing
 Is scandalous, by God, and that the poet
 Ought to be hanged for having the nerve to show it.

   (To Clitandre and Acaste, who are laughing.)

 By heaven, Sirs, I really didn't know
 That I was being humorous.

CÉLIMÈNE.   Go, Sir, go;
 Settle your business.

ALCESTE.   I shall, and when I'm through,
 I shall return to settle things with you.   30

ACT III

SCENE 1. (CLITANDRE, ACASTE)

CLITANDRE. Dear Marquess, how contented you appear;
 All things delight you, nothing mars your cheer.

Can you, in perfect honesty, declare
That you've a right to be so debonair?
ACASTE. By Jove, when I survey myself, I find
No cause whatever for distress of mind.
I'm young and rich; I can in modesty
Lay claim to an exalted pedigree;
And owing to my name and my condition
I shall not want for honors and position.   10
Then as to courage, that most precious trait,
I seem to have it, as was proved of late
Upon the field of honor, where my bearing,
They say, was very cool and rather daring.
I've wit, of course; and taste in such perfection
That I can judge without the least reflection,
And at the theater, which is my delight,
Can make or break a play on opening night,
And lead the crowd in hisses or bravos,
And generally be known as one who knows.   20
I'm clever, handsome, gracefully polite;
My waist is small, my teeth are strong and white;
As for my dress, the world's astonished eyes
Assure me that I bear away the prize.
I find myself in favor everywhere,
Honored by men, and worshipped by the fair;
And since these things are so, it seems to me
I'm justified in my complacency.
CLITANDRE. Well, if so many ladies hold you dear,
Why do you press a hopeless courtship here?   30
ACASTE. Hopeless, you say? I'm not the sort of fool
That likes his ladies difficult and cool.
Men who are awkward, shy, and peasantish
May pine for heartless beauties, if they wish,
Grovel before them, bear their cruelties,
Woo them with tears and sighs and bended knees,
And hope by dogged faithfulness to gain
What their poor merits never could obtain.
For men like me, however, it makes no sense
To love on trust, and foot the whole expense.   40
Whatever any lady's merits be,
I think, thank God, that I'm as choice as she;
That if my heart is kind enough to burn

For her, she owes me something in return;
And that in any proper love affair
The partners must invest an equal share.
CLITANDRE. You think, then, that our hostess favors you?
ACASTE. I've reason to believe that that is true.
CLITANDRE. How did you come to such a mad conclusion?
   You're blind, dear fellow. This is sheer delusion.   50
ACASTE. All right, then: I'm deluded and I'm blind.
CLITANDRE. Whatever put the notion in your mind?
ACASTE. Delusion.
CLITANDRE.   What persuades you that you're right?
ACASTE. I'm blind.
CLITANDRE.   But have you any proofs to cite?
ACASTE. I tell you I'm deluded.
CLITANDRE.   Have you, then,
   Received some secret pledge from Célimène?
ASCASTE. Oh, no: she scorns me.
CLITANDRE.   Tell me the truth, I beg.
ACASTE. She just can't bear me.
CLITANDRE.   Ah, don't pull my leg.
   Tell me what hope she's given you, I pray.
ACASTE. I'm hopeless, and it's you who win the day.   60
   She hates me thoroughly, and I'm so vexed
   I mean to hang myself on Tuesday next.
CLITANDRE. Dear Marquess, let us have an armistice
   And make a treaty. What do you say to this?
   If ever one of us can plainly prove
   That Célimène encourages his love,
   The other must abandon hope, and yield,
   And leave him in possession of the field.
ACASTE. Now, there's a bargain that appeals to me;
   With all my heart, dear Marquess, I agree.   70
   But hush.

SCENE 2. (CÉLIMÈNE, ACASTE, CLITANDRE)

CÉLIMÈNE. Still here?
CLITANDRE.   'Twas love that stayed our feet.
CÉLIMÈNE. I think I heard a carriage in the street.
   Whose is it? D'you know?

SCENE 3. (CÉLIMÈNE, ACASTE, CLITANDRE, BASQUE)

BASQUE.   Arsinoé is here,
  Madame.
CÈLIMÉNE. Arsinoé, you say? Oh, dear.
BASQUE. Éliante is entertaining her below.
CÉLIMÈNE. What brings the creature here, I'd like to know?
ACASTE. They say she's dreadfully prudish, but in fact
  I think her piety . . .
CÉLIMÈNE.   It's all an act.
  At heart she's worldly, and her poor success
  In snaring men explains her prudishness.
  It breaks her heart to see the beaux and gallants   10
  Engrossed by other women's charms and talents,
  And so she's always in a jealous rage
  Against the faulty standards of the age.
  She lets the world believe that she's a prude
  To justify her loveless solitude,
  And strives to put a brand of moral shame
  On all the graces that she cannot claim.
  But still she'd love a lover; and Alceste
  Appears to be the one she'd love the best.
  His visits here are poison to her pride;   20
  She seems to think I've lured him from her side;
  And everywhere, at court or in the town,
  The spiteful, envious woman runs me down.
  In short, she's just as stupid as can be,
  Vicious and arrogant in the last degree,
  And . . .

SCENE 4. (ARSINOÉ, CÉLIMÈNE, CLITANDRE, ACASTE)

CÉLIMÈNE. Ah! What happy chance has brought you here?
  I've thought about you ever so much, my dear.
ARSINOÉ. I've come to tell you something you should know.
CÉLIMÈNE. How good of you to think of doing so!

(*Clitandre and Acaste go out, laughing.*)

SCENE 5. (ARSINOÉ, CÉLIMÈNE)

ARSINOÉ. It's just as well those gentlemen didn't tarry.
CÉLIMÈNE. Shall we sit down?
ARSINOÉ.   That won't be necessary.
 Madam, the flame of friendship ought to burn
 Brightest in matters of the most concern,
 And as there's nothing which concerns us more
 Than honor, I have hastened to your door
 To bring you, as your friend, some information
 About the status of your reputation.
 I visited, last night, some virtuous folk,
 And, quite by chance, it was of you they spoke;   10
 There was, I fear, no tendency to praise
 Your light behavior and your dashing ways.
 The quantity of gentlemen you see
 And your by now notorious coquetry
 Were both so vehemently criticized
 By everyone, that I was much surprised.
 Of course, I needn't tell you where I stood;
 I came to your defense as best I could,
 Assured them you were harmless, and declared
 Your soul was absolutely unimpaired.   20
 But there are some things, you must realize,
 One can't excuse, however hard one tries,
 And I was forced at last into conceding
 That your behavior, Madam, is misleading,
 That it makes a bad impression, giving rise
 To ugly gossip and obscene surmise,
 And that if you were more *overtly* good,
 You wouldn't be so much misunderstood.
 Not that I think you've been unchaste—no! no!
 The saints preserve me from a thought so low!   30
 But mere good conscience never did suffice:
 One must avoid the outward show of vice.
 Madam, you're too intelligent, I'm sure,
 To think my motives anything but pure
 In offering you this counsel—which I do
 Out of a zealous interest in you.
CÉLIMÈNE. Madam, I haven't taken you amiss;

I'm very much obliged to you for this;
And I'll at once discharge the obligation
By telling you about *your* reputation.   40
You've been so friendly as to let me know
What certain people say of me, and so
I mean to follow your benign example
By offering you a somewhat similar sample.
The other day, I went to an affair
And found some most distinguished people there
Discussing piety, both false and true.
The conversation soon came round to you.
Alas! Your prudery and bustling zeal
Appeared to have a very slight appeal.   50
Your affectation of a grave demeanor,
Your endless talk of virtue and of honor,
The aptitude of your suspicious mind
For finding sin where there is none to find,
Your towering self-esteem, that pitying face
With which you contemplate the human race,
Your sermonizings and your sharp aspersions
On people's pure and innocent diversions—
All these were mentioned, Madam, and, in fact,
Were roundly and concertedly attacked.   60
"What good," they said, "are all these outward shows,
When everything belies her pious pose?
She prays incessantly; but then, they say,
She beats her maids and cheats them of their pay;
She shows her zeal in every holy place,
But still she's vain enough to paint her face;
She holds that naked statues are immoral,
But with a naked *man* she'd have no quarrel."
Of course, I said to everybody there
That they were being viciously unfair;   70
But still they were disposed to criticize you,
And all agreed that someone should advise you
To leave the morals of the world alone,
And worry rather more about your own.
They felt that one's self-knowledge should be great
Before one thinks of setting others straight;
That one should learn the art of living well
Before one threatens other men with hell,

And that the Church is best equipped, no doubt,
To guide our souls and root our vices out.   80
Madam, you're too intelligent, I'm sure,
To think my motives anything but pure
In offering you this counsel—which I do
Out of a zealous interest in you.
ARSINOÉ. I dared not hope for gratitude, but I
    Did not expect so acid a reply;
    I judge, since you've been so extremely tart,
    That my good counsel pierced you to the heart.
CÉLIMÈNE. Far from it, Madam. Indeed, it seems to me
    We ought to trade advice more frequently.   90
    One's vision of oneself is so defective
    That it would be an excellent corrective.
    If you are willing, Madam, let's arrange
    Shortly to have another frank exchange
    In which we'll tell each other, *entre nous,*
    What you've heard tell of me, and I of you.
ARSINOÉ. Oh, people never censure you, my dear;
    It's me they criticize. Or so I hear.
CÉLIMÈNE. Madam, I think we either blame or praise
    According to our taste and length of days.   100
    There is a time of life for coquetry,
    And there's a season, too, for prudery.
    When all one's charms are gone, it is, I'm sure,
    Good strategy to be devout and pure:
    It makes one seem a little less forsaken.
    Some day, perhaps, I'll take the road you've taken:
    Time brings all things. But I have aplenty,
    And see no cause to be a prude at twenty.
ARSINOÉ. You give your age in such a gloating tone
    That one would think I was an ancient crone;   110
    We're not so far apart, in sober truth,
    That you can mock me with a boast of youth!
    Madam, you baffle me. I wish I knew
    What moves you to provoke me as you do.
CÉLIMÈNE. For my part, Madam, I should like to know
    Why you abuse me everywhere you go.
    Is it my fault, dear lady, that your hand
    Is not, alas, in very great demand?
    If men admire me, if they pay me court

And daily make me offers of the sort   120
You'd dearly love to have them make to you,
How can I help it? What would you have me do?
If what you want is lovers, please feel free
To take as many as you can from me.

ARSINOÉ. Oh, come. D'you think the world is losing sleep
Over the flock of lovers which you keep,
Or that we find it difficult to guess
What price you pay for their devotedness?
Surely you don't expect us to suppose
Mere merit could attract so many beaux?   130
It's not your virtue that they're dazzled by;
Nor is it virtuous love for which they sigh.
You're fooling no one, Madam; the world's not blind;
There's many a lady heaven has designed
To call men's noblest, tenderest feelings out,
Who has no lovers dogging her about;
From which it's plain that lovers nowadays
Must be acquired in bold and shameless ways,
And only pay one court for such reward
As modesty and virtue can't afford.   140
Then don't be quite so puffed up, if you please,
About your tawdry little victories;
Try, if you can, to be a shade less vain,
And treat the world with somewhat less disdain.
If one were envious of your amours,
One soon could have a following like yours;
Lovers are no great trouble to collect
If one prefers them to one's self-respect.

CÉLIMÈNE. Collect them then, my dear; I'd love to see
You demonstrate that charming theory;   150
Who knows, you might . . .

ARSINOÉ.   Now, Madam, that will do;
It's time to end this trying interview.
My coach is late in coming to your door,
Or I'd have taken leave of you before.

CÉLIMÈNE. Oh, please don't feel that you must rush away;
I'd be delighted, Madam, if you'd stay.
However, lest my conversation bore you,
Let me provide some better company for you;
This gentleman, who comes most apropos,
Will please you more than I could do, I know.   160

SCENE 6. (ALCESTE, CÉLIMÈNE, ARSINOÉ)

CÉLIMÈNE. Alceste, I have a little note to write
  Which simply must go out before tonight;
  Please entertain *Madame;* I'm sure that she
  Will overlook my incivility.

SCENE 7. (ALCESTE, ARSINOÉ)

ARSINOÉ. Well, Sir, our hostess graciously contrives
  For us to chat until my coach arrives;
  And I shall be forever in her debt
  For granting me this little tête-à-tête.
  We women very rightly give our hearts
  To men of noble character and parts,
  And your especial merits, dear Alceste,
  Have roused the deepest sympathy in my breast.
  Oh, how I wish they had sufficient sense
  At court, to recognize your excellence!   10
  They wrong you greatly, Sir. How it must hurt you
  Never to be rewarded for your virtue!
ALCESTE. Why, Madam, what cause have I to feel aggrieved?
  What great and brilliant thing have I achieved?
  What service have I rendered to the King
  That I should look to him for anything?
ARSINOÉ. Not everyone who's honored by the State
  Has done great services. A man must wait
  Till time and fortune offer him the chance.
  Your merit, Sir, is obvious at a glance,   20
  And . . .
ALCESTE. Ah, forget my merit; I am not neglected.
  The court, I think, can hardly be expected
  To mine men's souls for merit, and unearth
  Our hidden virtues and our secret worth.
ARSINOÉ. *Some* virtues, though, are far too bright to hide;
  Yours are acknowledged, Sir, on every side.
  Indeed, I've heard you warmly praised of late
  By persons of considerable weight.
ALCESTE. This fawning age has praise for everyone,   30
  And all distinctions, Madam, are undone.

All things have equal honor nowadays,
And no one should be gratified by praise.
To be admired, one only need exist,
And every lackey's on the honors list.
ARSINOÉ. I only wish, Sir, that you had your eye
  On some position at court, however high;
  You'd only have to hint at such a notion
  For me to set the proper wheels in motion;
  I've certain friendships I'd be glad to use   40
  To get you any office you might choose.
ALCESTE. Madam, I fear that any such ambition
  Is wholly foreign to my disposition.
  The soul God gave me isn't of the sort
  That prospers in the weather of a court.
  It's all too obvious that I don't possess
  The virtues necessary for success.
  My one great talent is for speaking plain;
  I've never learned to flatter or to feign;
  And anyone so stupidly sincere   50
  Had best not seek a courtier's career.
  Outside the court, I know, one must dispense
  With honors, privilege, and influence;
  But still one gains the right, foregoing these,
  Not to be tortured by the wish to please.
  One needn't live in dread of snubs and slights,
  Nor praise the verse that every idiot writes,
  Nor humor silly Marquesses, nor bestow
  Politic sighs on Madam So-and-So.
ARSINOÉ. Forget the court, then; let the matter rest. 60
  But I've another cause to be distressed
  About your present situation, Sir.
  It's to your love affair that I refer.
  She whom you love, and who pretends to love you,
  Is, I regret to say, unworthy of you.
ALCESTE. Why, Madam? Can you seriously intend
  To make so grave a charge against your friend?
ARSINOÉ. Alas, I must. I've stood aside too long
  And let that lady do you grievous wrong;
  But now my debt to conscience shall be paid: 70
  I tell you that your love has been betrayed.
ALCESTE. I thank you, Madam; you're extremely kind.
  Such words are soothing to a lover's mind.

ARSINOÉ. Yes, though she *is* my friend, I say again
　You're very much too good for Célimène.
　She's wantonly misled you from the start.
ALCESTE. You may be right; who knows another's heart?
　But ask yourself if it's the part of charity
　To shake my soul with doubts of her sincerity.
ARSINOÉ. Well, if you'd rather be a dupe than doubt her, 　　80
　That's your affair. I'll say no more about her.
ALCESTE. Madam, you know that doubt and vague suspicion
　Are painful to a man in my position;
　It's most unkind to worry me this way
　Unless you've some real proof of what you say.
ARSINOÉ. Sir, say no more: all doubts shall be removed,
　And all that I've been saying shall be proved.
　You've only to escort me home, and there
　We'll look into the heart of this affair.
　I've ocular evidence which will persuade you 　　90
　Beyond a doubt, that Célimène's betrayed you.
　Then, if you're saddened by that revelation,
　Perhaps I can provide some consolation.

ACT IV

SCENE 1. (ÉLIANTE, PHILINTE)

PHILINTE. Madam, he acted like a stubborn child;
　I thought they never would be reconciled;
　In vain we reasoned, threatened, and appealed;
　He stood his ground and simply would not yield.
　The Marshals, I feel sure, have never heard
　An argument so splendidly absurd.
　"No gentlemen," said he, "I'll not retract.
　His verse is bad: extremely bad, in fact.
　Surely it does the man no harm to know it.
　Does it disgrace him, not to be a poet? 　　10
　A gentleman may be respected still,
　Whether he writes a sonnet well or ill.
　That I dislike his verse should not offend him;
　In all that touches honor, I commend him;

He's noble, brave, and virtuous—but I fear
He can't in truth be called a sonneteer.
I'll gladly praise his wardrobe; I'll endorse
His dancing, or the way he sits a horse;
But, gentlemen, I cannot praise his rhyme.
In fact, it ought to be a capital crime   20
For anyone so sadly unendowed
To write a sonnet, and read the thing aloud."
At length he fell into a gentler mood
And, striking a concessive attitude,
He paid Oronte the following courtesies:
"Sir, I regret that I'm so hard to please,
And I'm profoundly sorry that your lyric
Failed to provoke me to a panegyric."
After these curious words, the two embraced,
And then the hearing was adjourned—in haste.   30
ÉLIANTE. His conduct has been very singular lately;
  Still, I confess that I respect him greatly.
  The honesty in which he takes such pride
  Has—to my mind—it's noble, heroic side.
  In this false age, such candor seems outrageous;
  But I could wish that it were more contagious.
PHILINTE. What most intrigues me in our friend Alceste
  Is the grand passion that rages in his breast.
  The sullen humors he's compounded of
  Should not, I think, dispose his heart to love;   40
  But since they do, it puzzles me still more
  That he should choose your cousin to adore.
ÉLIANTE. It does, indeed, belie the theory
  That love is born of gentle sympathy,
  And that the tender passion must be based
  On sweet accords of temper and of taste.
PHILINTE. Does she return his love, do you suppose?
ÉLIANTE. Ah, that's a difficult question, Sir. Who knows?
  How can we judge the truth of her devotion?
  Her heart's a stranger to its own emotion.   50
  Sometimes it thinks it loves, when no love's there;
  At other times it loves quite unaware.
PHILINTE. I rather think Alceste is in for more
  Distress and sorrow than he's bargained for;
  Were he of my mind, Madam, his affection
  Would turn in quite a different direction,

And we would see him more responsive to
The kind regard which he receives from you.
ÉLIANTE. Sir, I believe in frankness, and I'm inclined,
   In matters of the heart, to speak my mind.   60
   I don't oppose his love for her; indeed,
   I hope with all my heart that he'll succeed,
   And were it in my power, I'd rejoice
   In giving him the lady of his choice.
   But if, as happens frequently enough
   In love affairs, he meets with a rebuff—
   If Célimène should grant some rival's suit—
   I'd gladly play the role of substitute;
   Nor would his tender speeches please me less
   Because they'd once been made without success.   70
PHILINTE. Well, Madam, as for me, I don't oppose
   Your hopes in this affair; and heaven knows
   That in my conversations with the man
   I plead your cause as often as I can.
   But if those two should marry, and so remove
   All chance that he will offer you his love,
   Then I'll declare my own, and hope to see
   Your gracious favor pass from him to me.
   In short, should you be cheated of Alceste,
   I'd be most happy to be second best.   80
ÉLIANTE. Philinte, you're teasing.
PHILINTE.   Ah, Madam, never fear;
   No words of mine were ever so sincere,
   And I shall live in fretful expectation
   Till I can make a fuller declaration.

SCENE 2. (ALCESTE, ÉLIANTE, PHILINTE)

ALCESTE. Avenge me, Madam! I must have satisfaction,
   Or this great wrong will drive me to distraction!
ÉLIANTE. Why, what's the matter? What's upset you so?
ALCESTE. Madam, I've had a mortal, mortal blow.
   If Chaos repossessed the universe,
   I'd swear I'd not be shaken any worse.
   I'm ruined. . . . I can say no more. . . . My soul . . .
ÉLIANTE. Do try, Sir, to regain your self-control.
ALCESTE. Just heaven! Why were so much beauty and grace

Bestowed on one so vicious and so base?   10
ÉLIANTE. Once more, Sir, tell us. . . .
ALCESTE.   My world has gone to wrack;
   I'm—I'm betrayed; she's stabbed me in the back:
   Yes, Célimène (who would have thought it of her?)
   Is false to me, and has another lover.
ÉLIANTE. Are you quite certain? Can you prove these things?
PHILINTE. Lovers are prey to wild imaginings
   And jealous fancies. No doubt there's some mistake. . . .
ALCESTE. Mind your own business, Sir, for heaven's sake.

(To Éliante.)

   Madam, I have the proof that you demand
   Here in my pocket, penned by her own hand.   20
   Yes, all the shameful evidence one could want
   Lies in this letter written to Oronte—
   Oronte! whom I felt sure she couldn't love,
   And hardly bothered to be jealous of.
PHILINTE. Still, in a letter, appearances may deceive;
   This may not be so bad as you believe.
ALCESTE. Once more I beg you, Sir, to let me be;
   Tend to your own affairs; leave mine to me.
ÉLIANTE. Compose yourself; this anguish that you feel . . .
ALCESTE. Is something, Madam, you alone can heal.   30
   My outraged heart, beside itself with grief,
   Appeals to you for comfort and relief.
   Avenge me on your cousin, whose unjust
   And faithless nature has deceived my trust;
   Avenge a crime your pure soul must detest.
ÉLIANTE. But how, Sir?
ALCESTE.   Madam, this heart within my breast
   Is yours; pray take it; redeem my heart from her,
   And so avenge me on my torturer.
   Let her be punished by the fond emotion,
   The ardent love, the bottomless devotion,   40
   The faithful worship which this heart of mine
   Will offer up to yours as to a shrine.
ÉLIANTE. You have my sympathy, Sir, in all you suffer;
   Nor do I scorn the noble heart you offer;
   But I suspect you'll soon be mollified,
   And this desire for vengeance will subside.

When some belovèd hand has done us wrong
We thirst for retribution—but not for long;
However dark the deed that she's committed,
A lovely culprit's very soon acquitted.   50
Nothing's so stormy as an injured lover,
And yet no storm so quickly passes over.
ALCESTE. No, Madam, no— this is no lovers' spat;
  I'll not forgive her; it's gone too far for that;
  My mind's made up; I'll kill myself before
  I waste my hopes upon her any more.
  Ah, here she is. My wrath intensifies.
  I shall confront her with her tricks and lies,
  And crush her utterly, and bring you then
  A heart no longer slave to Célimène.   60

SCENE 3. (CÉLIMÈNE, ALCESTE)

ALCESTE (*aside*). Sweet heaven, help me to control my passion.
CÉLIMÈNE (*aside*). Oh, Lord.
  (*To Alceste.*)
                        Why stand there staring in that fashion?
  And what d'you mean by those dramatic sighs,
  And that malignant glitter in your eyes?
ALCESTE. I mean that sins which cause the blood to freeze
  Look innocent beside your treacheries;
  That nothing Hell's or Heaven's wrath could do
  Ever produced so bad a thing as you.
CÉLIMÈNE. Your compliments were always sweet and pretty.
ALCESTE. Madam, it's not the moment to be witty.   10
  No, blush and hang your head; you've ample reason,
  Since I've the fullest evidence of your treason.
  Ah, this is what my sad heart prophesied;
  Now all my anxious fears are verified;
  My dark suspicion and my gloomy doubt
  Divined the truth, and now the truth is out.
  For all your trickery, I was not deceived;
  It was my bitter stars that I believed.
  But don't imagine that you'll go scot-free;
  You shan't misuse me with impunity.   20
  I know that love's irrational and blind;
  I know the heart's not subject to the mind,

And can't be reasoned into beating faster;
I know each soul is free to choose its master;
Therefore had you but spoken from the heart,
Rejecting my attentions from the start,
I'd have no grievance, or at any rate
I could complain of nothing but my fate.
Ah, but so falsely to encourage me—
That was a treason and a treachery   30
For which you cannot suffer too severely,
And you shall pay for that behavior dearly.
Yes, now I have no pity, not a shred;
My temper's out of hand; I've lost my head;
Shocked by the knowledge of your double-dealings,
My reason can't restrain my savage feelings;
A righteous wrath deprives me of my senses,
And I won't answer for the consequences.

CÉLIMÈNE. What does this outburst mean? Will you please explain?
    Have you, by any chance, gone quite insane?   40

ALCESTE. Yes, yes, I went insane the day I fell
    A victim to your black and fatal spell,
    Thinking to meet with some sincerity
    Among the treacherous charms that beckoned me.

CÉLIMÈNE. Pooh. Of what treachery can you complain?

ALCESTE. How sly you are, how cleverly you feign!
    But you'll not victimize me any more.
    Look: here's a document you've seen before.
    This evidence, which I acquired today,
    Leaves you, I think, without a thing to say.   50

CÉLIMÈNE. Is this what sent you into such a fit?

ALCESTE. You should be blushing at the sight of it.

CÉLIMÈNE. Ought I to blush? I truly don't see why.

ALCESTE. Ah, now you're being bold as well as sly;
    Since there's no signature, perhaps you'll claim . . .

CÉLIMÈNE. I wrote it, whether or not it bears my name.

ALCESTE. And you can view with equanimity
    This proof of your disloyalty to me!

CÉLIMÈNE. Oh, don't be so outrageous and extreme.

ALCESTE. You take this matter lightly, it would seem.   60
    Was it no wrong to me, no shame to you,
    That you should send Oronte this billet-doux?

CÉLIMÈNE. Oronte! Who said it was for him?

ALCESTE.   Why, those

Who brought me this example of your prose.
But what's the difference? If you wrote the letter
To someone else, it pleases me no better.
My grievance and your guilt remain the same.
CÉLIMÈNE. But need you rage, and need I blush for shame,
  If this was written to a *woman* friend?
ALCESTE. Ah! Most ingenious. I'm impressed no end;   70
  And after that incredible evasion
  Your guilt is clear. I need no more persuasion.
  How dare you try so clumsy a deception?
  D'you think I'm wholly wanting in perception?
  Come, come, let's see how brazenly you'll try
  To bolster up so palpable a lie:
  Kindly construe this ardent closing section
  As nothing more than sisterly affection!
  Here, let me read it. Tell me, if you dare to,
  That this is for a woman . . .
CÉLIMÈNE.   I don't care to.   80
  What right have you to badger and berate me,
  And so highhandedly interrogate me?
ALCESTE. Now, don't be angry; all I ask of you
  Is that you justify a phrase or two . . .
CÉLIMÈNE. No, I shall not. I utterly refuse,
  And you may take those phrases as you choose.
ALCESTE. Just show me how this letter could be meant
  For a woman's eyes, and I shall be content.
CÉLIMÈNE. No, no, it's for Oronte; you're perfectly right.   90
  I welcome his attentions with delight,
  I prize his character and his intellect,
  And everything is just as you suspect.
  Come, do your worst now; give your rage free rein;
  But kindly cease to bicker and complain.
ALCESTE (*aside*). Good God! Could anything be more inhuman?
  Was ever a heart so mangled by a woman?
  When I complain of how she has betrayed me,
  She bridles, and commences to upbraid me!
  She tries my tortured patience to the limit;   100
  She won't deny her guilt; she glories in it!
  And yet my heart's too faint and cowardly
  To break these chains of passion, and be free
  To scorn her as it could, and rise above
  This unrewarded, mad, and bitter love.

(To Célimène.)

Ah, traitress, in how confident a fashion
You take advantage of my helpless passion,
And use my weakness for your faithless charms
To make me once again throw down my arms!
But do at least deny this black transgression;
Take back that mocking and perverse confession;   110
Defend this letter and your innocence,
And I, poor fool, will aid in your defense.
Pretend, pretend, that you are just and true,
And I shall make myself believe in you.
CÉLIMÈNE. Oh, stop it. Don't be such a jealous dunce,
Or I shall leave off loving you at once.
Just why should I *pretend?* What could impel me
To stoop so low as that? And kindly tell me
Why, if I loved another, I shouldn't merely
Inform you of it, simply and sincerely!   120
I've told you where you stand, and that admission
Should altogether clear me of suspicion;
After so generous a guarantee,
What right have you to harbor doubts of me?
Since women are (from natural reticence)
Reluctant to declare their sentiments,
And since the honor of our sex requires
That we conceal our amorous desires,
Ought any man for whom such laws are broken
To question what the oracle has spoken?   130
Should he not rather feel an obligation
To trust that most obliging declaration?
Enough, now. Your suspicions quite disgust me;
Why should I love a man who doesn't trust me?
I cannot understand why I continue,
Fool that I am, to take an interest in you.
I ought to choose a man less prone to doubt,
And give you something to be vexed about.
ALCESTE. Ah, what a poor enchanted fool I am;
These gentle words, no doubt, were all a sham,   140
But destiny requires me to entrust
My happiness to you, and so I must.
I'll love you to the bitter end, and see
How false and treacherous you dare to be.

CÉLIMÈNE. No, you don't really love me as you ought.
ALCESTE. I love you more than can be said or thought;
   Indeed, I wish you were in such distress
   That I might show my deep devotedness.
   Yes, I could wish that you were wretchedly poor,
   Unloved, uncherished, utterly obscure;   150
   That fate had set you down upon the earth
   Without possessions, rank, or gentle birth;
   Then, by the offer of my heart, I might
   Repair the great injustice of your plight;
   I'd raise you from the dust, and proudly prove
   The purity and vastness of my love.
CÉLIMÈNE. This is a strange benevolence indeed!
   God grant that I may never be in need. . . .
   Ah, here's Monsieur Dubois, in quaint disguise.

SCENE 4. (CÉLIMÈNE, ALCESTE, DUBOIS)

ALCESTE. Well, why this costume? Why those frightened eyes?
   What ails you?
DUBOIS.   Well, Sir, things are most mysterious.
ALCESTE. What do you mean?
DUBOIS.   I fear they're very serious.
ALCESTE. What?
DUBOIS.   Shall I speak more loudly?
ALCESTE.   Yes; speak out.
DUBOIS. Isn't there someone here, Sir?
ALCESTE.   Speak, you lout!
   Stop wasting time.
DUBOIS.   Sir, we must slip away.
ALCESTE. How's that?
DUBOIS.   We must decamp without delay.
ALCESTE. Explain yourself.
DUBOIS.   I tell you we must fly.
ALCESTE. What for?
DUBOIS.   We mustn't pause to say good-by.
ALCESTE. Now what d'you mean by all of this, you clown?   10
DUBOIS. I mean, Sir, that we've got to leave this town.
ALCESTE. I'll tear you limb from limb and joint from joint
   If you don't come more quickly to the point.
DUBOIS. Well, Sir, today a man in a black suit,

Who wore a black and ugly scowl to boot,
Left us a document scrawled in such a hand
As even Satan couldn't understand.
It bears upon your lawsuit, I don't doubt;
But all hell's devils couldn't make it out.

ALCESTE. Well, well, go on. What then? I fail to see   20
How this event obliges us to flee.

DUBOIS. Well, Sir, an hour later, hardly more,
A gentleman who's often called before
Came looking for you in an anxious way.
Not finding you, he asked me to convey
(Knowing I could be trusted with the same)
The following message. . . . Now, what *was* his name?

ALCESTE. Forget his name, you idiot. What did he say?

DUBOIS. Well, it was one of your friends, Sir, anyway.
He warned you to begone, and he suggested   30
That if you stay, you may well be arrested.

ALCESTE. What? Nothing more specific? Think, man, think!

DUBOIS. No, Sir. He had me bring him pen and ink,
And dashed you off a letter which, I'm sure,
Will render things distinctly less obscure.

ALCESTE. Well—let me have it!

CÉLIMÈNE.   What *is* this all about?

ALCESTE. God knows; but I have hopes of finding out.
How long am I to wait, you blitherer?

DUBOIS. (*after a protracted search for the letter*). I must have left it
on your table, Sir.

ALCESTE. I ought to . . .

CÉLIMÈNE.   No, no, keep your self-control;   40
Go find out what's behind his rigmarole.

ALCESTE. It seems that fate, no matter what I do,
Has sworn that I may not converse with you;
But, Madam, pray permit your faithful lover
To try once more before the day is over.

ACT V

SCENE 1. (ALCESTE, PHILINTE)

ALCESTE. No, it's too much. My mind's made up, I tell you.

PHILINTE. Why should this blow, however hard, compel you . . .

ALCESTE. No, no, don't waste your breath in argument;
    Nothing you say will alter my intent;
    This age is vile, and I've made up my mind
    To have no further commerce with mankind.
    Did not truth, honor, decency, and the laws
    Oppose my enemy and approve my cause?
    My claims were justified in all men's sight;
    I put my trust in equity and right;   10
    Yet, to my horror and the world's disgrace,
    Justice is mocked, and I have lost my case!
    A scoundrel whose dishonesty is notorious
    Emerges from another lie victorious!
    Honor and right condone his brazen fraud,
    While rectitude and decency applaud!
    Before his smirking face, the truth stands charmed,
    And virtue conquered, and the law disarmed!
    His crime is sanctioned by a court decree!
    And not content with what he's done to me,   20
    The dog now seeks to ruin me by stating
    That I composed a book now circulating,
    A book so wholly criminal and vicious
    That even to speak its title is seditious!
    Meanwhile Oronte, my rival, lends his credit
    To the same libelous t.. ., and helps to spread it!
    Oronte! a man of honor and of rank,
    With whom I've been entirely fair and frank;
    Who sought me out and forced me, willy-nilly,
    To judge some verse I found extremely silly;   30
    And who, because I properly refused
    To flatter him, or see the truth abused,
    Abets my enemy in a rotten slander!
    There's the reward of honesty and candor!
    The man will hate me to the end of time
    For failing to commend his wretched rhyme!
    And not this man alone, but all humanity
    Do what they do from interest and vanity;
    They prate of honor, truth, and righteousness,
    But lie, betray, and swindle nonetheless.   40
    Come then: man's villainy is too much to bear;
    Let's leave this jungle and this jackal's lair.
    Yes! treacherous and savage race of men,
    You shall not look upon my face again.
PHILINTE. Oh, don't rush into exile prematurely;

Things aren't as dreadful as you make them, surely.
It's rather obvious, since you're still at large,
That people don't believe your enemy's charge.
Indeed, his tale's so patently untrue
That it may do more harm to him than you.   50
ALCESTE. Nothing could do that scoundrel any harm:
    His frank corruption is his greatest charm,
    And, far from hurting him, a further shame
    Would only serve to magnify his name.
PHILINTE. In any case, his bald prevarication
    Has done no injury to your reputation,
    And you may feel secure in that regard.
    As for your lawsuit, it should not be hard
    To have the case reopened, and contest
    This judgment . . .
ALCESTE.   No, no, let the verdict rest.   60
    Whatever cruel penalty it may bring,
    I wouldn't have it changed for anything.
    It shows the times' injustice with such clarity
    That I shall pass it down to our posterity
    As a great proof and signal demonstration
    Of the black wickedness of this generation.
    It may cost twenty thousand francs; but I
    Shall pay their twenty thousand, and gain thereby
    The right to storm and rage at human evil,
    And send the race of mankind to the devil.   70
PHILINTE. Listen to me . . .
ALCESTE.   Why? What can you possibly say?
    Don't argue, Sir; your labor's thrown away.
    Do you propose to offer lame excuses
    For men's behavior and the times' abuses?
PHILINTE. No, all you say I'll readily concede:
    This is a low, conniving age indeed;
    Nothing but trickery prospers nowadays,
    And people ought to mend their shabby ways.
    Yes, man's a beastly creature; but must we then
    Abandon the society of men?   80
    Here in the world, each human frailty
    Provides occasion for philosophy,
    And that is virtue's noblest exercise;
    If honesty shone forth from all men's eyes,
    If every heart were frank and kind and just.
    What could our virtues do but gather dust

(Since their employment is to help us bear
The villainies of men without despair) ?
A heart well-armed with virtue can endure. . . .
ALCESTE. Sir, you're a matchless reasoner, to be sure;   90
    Your words are fine and full of cogency;
    But don't waste time and eloquence on me.
    My reason bids me go, for my own good.
    My tongue won't lie and flatter as it should;
    God knows what frankness it might next commit,
    And what I'd suffer on account of it.
    Pray let me wait for Célimène's return
    In peace and quiet. I shall shortly learn,
    By her response to what I have in view,
    Whether her love for me is feigned or true.   100
PHILINTE. Till then, let's visit Éliante upstairs.
ALCESTE. No, I am too weighed down with somber cares.
    Go to her, do; and leave me with my gloom
    Here in the darkened corner of this room.
PHILINTE. Why, that's no sort of company, my friend;
    I'll see if Éliante will not descend.

SCENE 2. (CÉLIMÈNE, ORONTE, ALCESTE)

ORONTE. Yes, Madam, if you wish me to remain
    Your true and ardent lover, you must deign
    To give me some more positive assurance.
    All this suspense is quite beyond endurance.
    If your heart shares the sweet desires of mine,
    Show me as much by some convincing sign;
    And here's the sign I urgently suggest:
    That you no longer tolerate Alceste,
    But sacrifice him to my love, and sever
    All your relations with the man forever.   10
CÉLIMÈNE. Why do you suddenly dislike him so?
    You praised him to the skies not long ago.
ORONTE. Madam, that's not the point. I'm here to find
    Which way your tender feelings are inclined.
    Choose, if you please, between Alceste and me,
    And I shall stay or go accordingly.
ALCESTE. (*emerging from the corner*). Yes, Madam, choose; this gentle-
    man's demand
    Is wholly just, and I support his stand.

I too am true and ardent; I too am here
To ask you that you make your feelings clear.   20
No more delays, now; no equivocation;
The time has come to make your declaration.
ORONTE. Sir, I've no wish in any way to be
    An obstacle to your felicity.
ALCESTE. Sir, I've no wish to share her heart with you;
    That may sound jealous, but at least it's true.
ORONTE. If, weighing us, she leans in your direction . . .
ALCESTE. If she regards you with the least affection . . .
ORONTE. I swear I'll yield her to you there and then.
ALCESTE. I swear I'll never see her face again.   30
ORONTE. Now, Madam, tell us what we've come to hear.
ALCESTE. Madam, speak openly and have no fear.
ORONTE. Just say which one is to remain your lover.
ALCESTE. Just name one name, and it will all be over.
ORONTE. What! Is it possible that you're undecided?
ALCESTE. What! Can your feelings possibly be divided?
CÉLIMÈNE. Enough: this inquisition's gone too far:
    How utterly unreasonable you are!
    Not that I couldn't make the choice with ease;
    My heart has no conflicting sympathies;   40
    I know full well which one of you I favor,
    And you'd not see me hesitate or waver.
    But how can you expect me to reveal
    So cruelly and bluntly what I feel?
    I think it altogether too unpleasant
    To choose between two men when both are present;
    One's heart has means more subtle and more kind
    Of letting its affections be divined,
    Nor need one be uncharitably plain
    To let a lover know he loves in vain.   50
ORONTE. No, no, speak plainly; I for one can stand it.
    I beg you to be frank.
ALCESTE.   And I demand it.
    The simple truth is what I wish to know,
    And there's no need for softening the blow.
    You've made an art of pleasing everyone,
    But now your days of coquetry are done:
    You have no choice now, Madam, but to choose,
    For I'll know what to think if you refuse;
    I'll take your silence for a clear admission

That I'm entitled to my worst suspicion. 60
ORONTE. I thank you for this ultimatum, Sir,
  And I may say I heartily concur.
CÉLIMÈNE. Really, this foolishness is very wearing:
  Must you be so unjust and overbearing?
  Haven't I told you why I must demur?
  Ah, here's Éliante; I'll put the case to her.

SCENE 3. (ÉLIANTE, PHILINTE, CÉLIMÈNE, ORONTE,
          ALCESTE)

CÉLIMÈNE. Cousin, I'm being persecuted here
  By these two persons, who, it would appear,
  Will not be satisfied till I confess
  Which one I love the more, and which the less,
  And tell the latter to his face that he
  Is henceforth banished from my company.
  Tell me, has ever such a thing been done?
ÉLIANTE. You'd best not turn to me; I'm not the one
  To back you in a matter of this kind:
  I'm all for those who frankly speak their mind.
ORONTE. Madam, you'll search in vain for a defender.
ALCESTE. You're beaten, Madam, and may as well surrender.
ORONTE. Speak, speak, you must; and end this awful strain.
ALCESTE. Or don't, and your position will be plain.
ORONTE. A single word will close this painful scene.
ALCESTE. But if you're silent, I'll know what you mean.

SCENE 4. (ARSINOÉ, CÉLIMÈNE, ÉLIANTE, ALCESTE,
          PHILINTE, ACASTE, CLITANDRE, ORONTE)

ACASTE (*to Célimène*). Madam, with all due deference, we two
  Have come to pick a little bone with you.
CLITANDRE (*to Oronte and Alceste*). I'm glad you're present, Sirs, as
      you'll soon learn,
  Our business here is also your concern.
ARSINOÉ (*to Célimène*). Madam, I visit you so soon again
  Only because of these two gentlemen,
  Who came to me indignant and aggrieved
  About a crime too base to be believed.

Knowing your virtue, having such confidence in it,
I couldn't think you guilty for a minute,   10
In spite of all their telling evidence;
And, rising above our little difference,
I've hastened here in friendship's name to see
You clear yourself of this great calumny.
ACASTE. Yes, Madam, let us see with what composure
   You'll manage to respond to this disclosure.
   You lately sent Clitandre this tender note.
CLITANDRE. And this one, for Acaste, you also wrote.
ACASTE (*to Oronte and Alceste*). You'll recognize this writing, Sirs, I
      think;
The lady is so free with pen and ink   20
That you must know it all too well, I fear.
But listen: this is something you should hear.
   "How absurd you are to condemn my lightheartedness in so-
ciety, and to accuse me of being happiest in the company of others.
Nothing could be more unjust; and if you do not come to me
instantly and beg pardon for saying such a thing, I shall never
forgive you as long as I live. Our big bumbling friend the
Viscount . . ."
What a shame that he's not here.
   "Our big bumbling friend the Viscount, whose name stands   30
first in your complaint, is hardly a man to my taste; and ever
since the day I watched him spend three-quarters of an hour
spitting into a well, so as to make circles in the water, I have been
unable to think highly of him. As for the little Marquess . . ."
In all modesty, gentlemen, that is I.
   "As for the little Marquess, who sat squeezing my hand for such
a long while yesterday, I find him in all respects the most trifling
creature alive; and the only things of value about him are his cape
and his sword. As for the man with the green ribbons . . ."
(*To Alceste.*) It's your turn now, Sir.   40
   "As for the man with the green ribbons, he amuses me now and
then with his bluntness and his bearish ill-humor; but there are
many times indeed when I think him the greatest bore in the world.
And as for the sonneteer . . ."
(*To Oronte.*) Here's your helping.
   "And as for the sonneteer, who has taken it into his head to be
witty, and insists on being an author in the teeth of opinion, I
simply cannot be bothered to listen to him, and his prose wearies
me quite as much as his poetry. Be assured that I am not always

so well-entertained as you suppose; that I long for your company,   50
more than I dare to say, at all these entertainments to which people
drag me; and that the presence of those one loves is the true and
perfect seasoning to all one's pleasures."
CLITANDRE. And now for me.

"Clitandre, whom you mention, and who so pesters me with his
saccharine speeches, is the last man on earth for whom I could
feel any affection. He is quite mad to suppose that I love him, and
so are you, to doubt that you are loved. Do come to your senses;
exchange your suppositions for his; and visit me as often as pos-
sible, to help me bear the annoyance of his unwelcome attentions."   60
It's sweet character that these letters show,
And what to call it, Madam, you well know.
Enough. We're off to make the world acquainted
With this sublime self-portrait that you've painted.
ACASTE. Madam, I'll make you no farewell oration;
No, you're not worthy of my indignation.
Far choicer hearts than yours, as you'll discover,
Would like this little Marquess for a lover.

SCENE 5. (CÉLIMÈNE, ÉLIANTE, ARSINOÉ, ALCESTE,
ORONTE, PHILINTE)

ORONTE. So! After all those loving letters you wrote,
You turn on me like this, and cut my throat!
And your dissembling, faithless heart, I find,
Has pledged itself by turns to all mankind!
How blind I've been! But now I clearly see;
I thank you, Madam, for enlightening me.
My heart is mine once more, and I'm content;
The loss of it shall be your punishment.

(*To Alceste.*)

Sir, she is yours; I'll seek no more to stand
Between your wishes and this lady's hand.

SCENE 6. (CÉLIMÈNE, ÉLIANTE, ARSINOÉ, ALCESTE,
PHILINTE)

ARSINOÉ (*to Célimène*). Madam, I'm forced to speak. I'm far too stirred

To keep my counsel, after what I've heard.
I'm shocked and staggered by your want of morals.
It's not my way to mix in others' quarrels;
But really, when this fine and noble spirit,
This man of honor and surpassing merit,
Laid down the offering of his heart before you,
How *could* you . . .

ALCESTE.   Madam, permit me, I implore you,
To represent myself in this debate.
Don't bother, please, to be my advocate.   10
My heart, in any case, could not afford
To give your services their due reward;
And if I chose, for consolation's sake,
Some other lady, 'twould not be you I'd take.

ARSINOÉ. What makes you think you could, Sir? And how dare you
Imply that I've been trying to ensnare you?
If you can for a moment entertain
Such flattering fancies, you're extremely vain.
I'm not so interested as you suppose
In Célimène's discarded gigolos.   20
Get rid of that absurd illusion, do.
Women like me are not for such as you.
Stay with this creature, to whom you're so attached;
I've never seen two people better matched.

SCENE 7. (CÉLIMÈNE, ÉLIANTE, ALCESTE, PHILINTE)

ALCESTE (*to Célimène*). Well, I've been still throughout this exposé,
Till everyone but me has said his say.
Come, have I shown sufficient self-restraint?
And may I now . . .

CÉLIMÈNE.   Yes, make your just complaint.
Reproach me freely, call me what you will;
You've every right to say I've used you ill.
I've wronged you, I confess it; and in my shame
I'll make no effort to escape the blame.
The anger of those others I could despise;
My guilt toward you I sadly recognize.   10
Your wrath is wholly justified, I fear;
I know how culpable I must appear,
I know all things bespeak my treachery,

And that, in short, you've grounds for hating me.
Do so; I give you leave.
ALCESTE.   Ah, traitress—how,
How should I cease to love you, even now?
Though mind and will were passionately bent
On hating you, my heart would not consent.

(To Éliante and Philinte.)

Be witness to my madness, both of you;
See what infatuation drives one to;   20
But wait; my folly's only just begun,
And I shall prove to you before I'm done
How strange the human heart is, and how far
From rational we sorry creatures are.

To Célimène.)

Woman, I'm willing to forget your shame,
And clothe your treacheries in a sweeter name;
I'll call them youthful errors, instead of crimes,
And lay the blame on these corrupting times.
My one condition is that you agree
To share my chosen fate, and fly with me   30
To that wild, trackless, solitary place
In which I shall forget the human race.
Only by such a course can you atone
For those atrocious letters; by that alone
Can you remove my present horror of you,
And make it possible for me to love you.
CÉLIMÈNE. What! *I* renounce the world at my young age,
And die of boredom in some hermitage?
ALCESTE. Ah, if you really loved me as you ought,
You wouldn't give the world a moment's thought;   40
Must you have me, and all the world beside?
CÉLIMÈNE. Alas, at twenty one is terrified
Of solitude. I fear I lack the force
And depth of soul to take so stern a course.
But if my hand in marriage will content you,
Why, there's a plan which I might well consent to,
And . . .
ALCESTE. No, I detest you now. I could excuse

Everything else, but since you thus refuse
To love me wholly, as a wife should do,
And see the world in me, as I in you,   50
Go! I reject your hand, and disenthrall
My heart from your enchantments, once for all.

SCENE 8. (ÉLIANTE, ALCESTE, PHILINTE)

ALCESTE *(to Éliante)*. Madam, your virtuous beauty has no peer;
Of all this world you only are sincere;
I've long esteemed you highly, as you know;
Permit me ever to esteem you so,
And if I do not now request your hand,
Forgive me, Madam, and try to understand.
I feel unworthy of it; I sense that fate
Does not intend me for the married state,
That I should do you wrong by offering you
My shattered heart's unhappy residue,   10
And that in short . . .
ÉLIANTE.   Your argument's well taken:
Nor need you fear that I shall feel forsaken.
Were I to offer him this hand of mine,
Your friend Philinte, I think, would not decline.
PHILINTE. Ah, Madam, that's my heart's most cherished goal,
For which I'd gladly give my life and soul.
ALCESTE *(to Éliante and Philinte)*. May you be true to all you now profess,
And so deserve unending happiness.
Meanwhile, betrayed and wronged in everything,
I'll flee this bitter world where vice is king,   20
And seek some spot unpeopled and apart
Where I'll be free to have an honest heart.
PHILINTE. Come, Madam, let's do everything we can
To change the mind of this unhappy man.

Questions for Discussion

1. Molière's theatrical art was the outgrowth of a popular tradition called *commedia dell'arte*, which spread from Italy all over Europe in the late Renaissance. The characters were fixed types. To what extent has Molière continued this tradition in his characters?

2. Does the society which Molière writes about here seem to have a reasonable set of standards by which to judge behavior?

3. How does Alceste think that men should conduct themselves in society? Does he always follow his own theory?

4. Is Alceste's "frankness" about Oronte's sonnet unbiased?

5. The German poet Goethe considered *The Misanthrope* a tragedy. Is Alceste potentially a tragic hero?

6. What point of view does Philinte represent? Is it more acceptable than Alceste's "frankness"?

7. What does Scene 5 of Act II reveal about Célimène?

8. What is Ansinoé's attitude toward Célimène? See Scene 5 of Act III. Is Ansinoé a very "moral" person?

9. What does Éliante represent in the play? Does the author appear to criticize her in any way?

10. Is Alceste's final action a solution to his problems?

Alexander Pope (1688-1744)

The Rape of the Lock

CANTO I

What dire offense from am'rous causes springs,
What mighty contests rise from trivial things,
I sing—This verse to CARYL,[1] Muse! is due:
This, even Belinda may vouchsafe to view:
Slight is the subject, but not so the praise,
If she inspire, and he approve my lays.
  Say what strange motive, Goddess! could compel
A well-bred lord t' assault a gentle belle?
O say what stranger cause, yet unexplored,
Could make a gentle belle reject a lord?   10
In tasks so bold, can little men engage,
And in soft bosoms dwells such mighty rage?
  Sol through white curtains shot a tim'rous ray,
And oped those eyes that must eclipse the day:
Now lap-dogs give themselves the rousing shake,
And sleepless lovers, just at twelve, awake:
Thrice rung the bell, the slipper knocked the ground,
And the pressed watch[2] returned a silver sound.
Belinda still her downy pillow prest,
Her guardian sylph[3] prolonged the balmy rest: 20
'Twas he had summoned to her silent bed
The morning-dream that hovered o'er her head;
A youth more glitt'ring than a Birth-night beau,[4]

---

[1] John Caryll. He suggested that Pope write *The Rape of the Lock* in order to alleviate the conflict between the two families involved in the actual incident in which Lord Petre snipped a lock of hair from Arabella Fermor.

[2] A repeater watch. It rang the hour when pressed by a finger.

[3] According to the Rosicrucians the four elements of air, earth, water, and fire are inhabited respectively by Sylphs, Gnomes, Nymphs, and Salamanders. Sylphs also protected a woman's chastity.

[4] A gentleman dressed in a splendid way for a ball at court to celebrate a royal birthday.

(That even in slumber caused her cheek to glow)
Seemed to her ear his winning lips to lay,
And thus in whispers said, or seemed to say:
    Fairest of mortals, thou distinguished care
Of thousand bright inhabitants of air!
If e'er one vision touched thy infant thought;
Of all the nurse and all the priest have taught; 30
Of airy elves by moonlight shadows seen,
The silver token, and the circled green,[5]
Or virgins visited by angel-powers,
With golden crowns and wreaths of heav'nly flowers;
Hear and believe! thy own importance know,
Nor bound thy narrow views to things below.
Some secret truths, from learned pride concealed,
To maids alone and children are revealed:
What though no credit doubting wits may give?
The fair and innocent shall still believe. 40
Know, then, unnumbered spirits round thee fly,
The light militia of the lower sky:
These, though unseen, are ever on the wing,
Hang o'er the box, and hover round the ring.[6]
Think what an equipage thou hast in air.
And view with scorn two pages and a chair.[7]
As now your own, our beings were of old,
And once inclosed in woman's beauteous mould;
Thence, by a soft transition, we repair
From earthly vehicles to these of air. 50
Think not, when woman's transient breath is fled,
That all her vanities at once are dead;
Succeeding vanities she still regards,
And though she plays no more, o'erlooks the cards.
Her joy in gilded chariot, when alive,
And love of ombre[8] after death survive.
For when the fair in all their pride expire,
To their first elements their souls retire:[9]
The sprites of fiery termagants in flame
Mount up, and take a salamander's name. 60

---

[5] A coin or circle left by the fairies in the grass.
[6] The "box" in the theater and the fashionable "ring" or drive in Hyde Park.
[7] Sedan chair.
[8] A fashionable card game.
[9] See note 3.

Soft yielding minds to water glide away,
And sip, with nymphs, their elemental tea.
The graver prude sinks downward to a gnome,
In search of mischief still on earth to roam.
The light coquettes in sylphs aloft repair,
And sport and flutter in the fields of air.
 Know further yet; whoever fair and chaste
Rejects mankind, is by some sylph embraced:
For spirits, freed from mortal laws, with ease
Assume what sexes and what shapes they please.   70
What guards the purity of melting maids,
In courtly balls, and midnight masquerades,
Safe from the treach'rous friend, the daring spark,[10]
The glance by day, the whisper in the dark,
When kind occasion prompts their warm desires,
When music softens, and when dancing fires?
'Tis but their sylph, the wise celestials know,
Though honor is the word with men below.
 Some nymphs there are, too conscious of their face,
For life predestined to the gnomes' embrace.   80
These swell their prospects and exalt their pride,
When offers are disdained, and love denied:
Then gay ideas crowd the vacant brain,
While Peers, and Dukes, and all their sweeping train,
And Garters, Stars, and Coronets appear,[11]
And in soft sounds, "Your Grace" salutes their ear.
'Tis these that early taint the female soul,
Instruct the eyes of young coquettes to roll,
Teach infant-cheeks a bidden blush to know,
And little hearts to flutter at a beau.   90
 Oft, when the world imagine women stray,
The sylphs through mystic mazes guide their way,
Through all the giddy circle they pursue,
And old impertinence expel by new.
What tender maid but must a victim fall
To one man's treat, but for another's ball?
When Florio speaks what virgin could withstand,
If gentle Damon[12] did not squeeze her hand?
With varying vanities, from every part,
They shift the moving toyshop of their heart;   100

---

[10] A derogatory name for a showy or lively man about town.
[11] Symbols of noble rank.
[12] Conventional names for characters in pastoral love poems.

Where wigs with wigs, with sword-knots sword-knots strive,
Beaux banish beaux, and coaches coaches drive.
This erring mortals levity may call;
Oh blind to truth! the sylphs contrive it all.
　Of these am I, who thy protection claim,
A watchful sprite, and Ariel is my name.
Late, as I ranged the crystal wilds of air,
In the clear mirror of thy ruling star,
I saw, alas! some dread event impend,
Ere to the main this morning sun descend,　　　　110
But heaven reveals not what, or how, or where:
Warned by the sylph, oh pious maid, beware!
This to disclose is all thy guardian can:
Beware of all, but most beware of man!
　He said; when Shock,[13] who thought she slept too long,
Leaped up, and waked his mistress with his tongue.
'Twas then, Belinda, if report say true,
Thy eyes first opened on a billet-doux,[14]
Wounds, charms, and ardors were no sooner read,
But all the vision vanished from thy head.　　　　120
　And now, unveiled, the toilet[15] stands displayed,
Each silver vase in mystic order laid.
First, robed in white, the nymph intent adores,
With head uncovered, the cosmetic powers.
A heav'nly image in the glass appears,
To that she bends, to that her eyes she rears;
Th' inferior priestess, at her altar's side,
Trembling begins the sacred rites of Pride.
Unnumbered treasures ope at once, and here
The various off'rings of the world appear;　　　　130
From each she nicely culls with curious toil,
And decks the goddess with the glitt'ring spoil.
This casket India's glowing gems unlocks,
And all Arabia breathes from yonder box.
The tortoise here and elephant unite,
Transformed to combs, the speckled, and the white.
Here files of pins extend their shining rows,
Puffs, powders, patches,[16] Bibles, billet-doux.
Now awful Beauty puts on all its arms;

---

[13] A lapdog.
[14] A love letter.
[15] A dressing table.
[16] Beauty patches worn on the face.

The fair each moment rises in her charms,   140
Repairs her smiles, awakens every grace,
And calls forth all the wonders of her face;
Sees by degrees a purer blush arise,
And keener lightnings quicken in her eyes.
The busy sylphs surround their darling care,
These set the head, and those divide the hair,
Some fold the sleeve, whilst others plait the gown;
And Betty's[17] praised for labors not her own.

CANTO II

Not with more glories, in th' ethereal plain,
The Sun first rises o'er the purpled main,
Than issuing forth, the rival of his beams
Launched on the bosom of the silver Thames.
Fair nymphs, and well-drest youths around her shone,
But every eye was fixed on her alone.
On her white breast a sparkling cross she wore,
Which Jews might kiss, and infidels adore.
Her lively looks a sprightly mind disclose,
Quick as her eyes, and as unfixed as those: 10
Favors to none, to all she smiles extends;
Oft she rejects, but never once offends.
Bright as the sun, her eyes the gazers strike,
And, like the sun, they shine on all alike.
Yet graceful ease, and sweetness void of pride,
Might hide her faults, if belles had faults to hide:
If to her share some female errors fall,
Look on her face, and you'll forget 'em all.
   This nymph, to the destruction of mankind,
Nourished two locks, which graceful hung behind   20
In equal curls, and well conspired to deck
With shining ringlets the smooth iv'ry neck.
Love in these labyrinths his slaves detains,
And mighty hearts are held in slender chains.
With hairy springes[1] we the birds betray,
Slight lines of hair surprise the finny prey,[2]

---

17 Conventional name for a lady's maid.
1 Snares.
2 Fish.

Fair tresses man's imperial race ensnare,
And beauty draws us with a single hair.
Th' advent'rous baron the bright locks admired;
He saw, he wished, and to the prize aspired.   30
Resolved to win, he meditates the way,
By force to ravish, or by fraud betray;
For when success a lover's toil attends,
Few ask, if fraud or force attained his ends.
For this, ere Phœbus rose, he had implored
Propitious heaven, and every power adored,
But chiefly Love—to Love an altar built,
Of twelve vast French romances, neatly gilt.
There lay three garters, half a pair of gloves;
And all the trophies of his former loves;   40
With tender billet-doux he lights the pyre,
And breathes three am'rous sighs to raise the fire.
Then prostrate falls, and begs with ardent eyes
Soon to obtain, and long possess the prize:
The powers gave ear, and granted half his prayer,
The rest, the winds dispersed in empty air.
But now secure the painted vessel glides,
The sun-beams trembling on the floating tides:
While melting music steals upon the sky,
And softened sounds along the waters die;   50
Smooth flow the waves, the zephyrs gently play,
Belinda smiled, and all the world was gay.
All but the sylph—with careful thoughts opprest,
Th' impending woe sat heavy on his breast.
He summons strait his denizens of air;
The lucid squadrons round the sails repair:
Soft o'er the shrouds aërial whispers breathe,
That seemed but zephyrs to the train beneath.
Some to the sun their insect-wings unfold,
Waft on the breeze, or sink in clouds of gold;   60
Transparent forms, too fine for mortal sight,
Their fluid bodies half dissolved in light,
Loose to the wind their airy garments flew,
Thin glitt'ring textures of the filmy dew,
Dipt in the richest tincture of the skies,
Where light disports in ever-mingling dyes,
While every beam new transient colors flings,
Colors that change when'er they wave their wings.

Amid the circle on the gilded mast,
Superior by the head, was Ariel placed;   70
His purple pinions opening to the sun,
He raised his azure wand, and thus begun:
   Ye sylphs and sylphids, to your chief give ear!
Fays, fairies, genii, elves, and dæmons, hear!
Ye know the spheres and various tasks assigned
By laws eternal to th' aërial kind.
Some in the fields of purest æther play,
And bask and whiten in the blaze of day.
Some guide the course of wand'ring orbs on high,
Or roll the planets through the boundless sky.   80
Some less refined, beneath the moon's pale light
Pursue the stars that shoot athwart the night,
Or suck the mists in grosser air below,
Or dip their pinions in the painted bow,[3]
Or brew fierce tempests on the wintry main,
Or o'er the glebe[4] distil the kindly rain.
Others on earth o'er human race preside,
Watch all their ways, and all their actions guide:
Of these the chief the care of nations own,
And guard with arms divine the British throne.   90
   Our humbler province is to tend the fair,
Not a less pleasing, though less glorious care;
To save the powder from too rude a gale,
Nor let th' imprisoned essences exhale;
To draw fresh colors from the vernal flowers;
To steal from rainbows, e'er they drop in showers,
A brighter wash;[5] to curl their waving hairs,
Assist their blushes, and inspire their airs;
Nay, oft, in dreams, invention we bestow,
To change a flounce, or add a furbelow.   100
   This day, black omens threat the brightest fair,
That e'er deserved a watchful spirit's care;
Some dire disaster, or by force, or slight;
But what, or where, the fates have wrapt in night.
Whether the nymph shall break Diana's law,[6]
Or some frail china jar receive a flaw;

---

[3] Rainbow.
[4] Cultivated field.
[5] Cosmetic lotion.
[6] Diana was the goddess of chastity.

Or stain her honor, or her new brocade;
Forget her prayers, or miss a masquerade;
Or lose her heart, or necklace, at a ball;
Or whether heaven has doomed that Shock must fall.   110
Haste, then, ye spirits! to your charge repair:
The flutt'ring fan be Zephyretta's care;
The drops[7] to thee, Brillante, we consign;
And, Momentilla, let the watch be thine;
Do thou, Crispissa,[8] tend her fav'rite lock;
Ariel himself shall be the guard of Shock.
    To fifty chosen sylphs, of special note,
We trust th' important charge, the petticoat:
Oft have we known that seven-fold fence to fail,
Though stiff with hoops, and armed with ribs of whale,   120
Form a strong line about the silver bound,
And guard the wide circumference around.
    Whatever spirit, careless of his charge,
His post neglects, or leaves the fair at large,
Shall feel sharp vengeance soon o'ertake his sins,
Be stopped in vials, or transfixed with pins;
Or plunged in lakes of bitter washes lie,
Or wedged whole ages in a bodkin's eye:[9]
Gums and pomatums shall his flight restrain,
While clogged he beats his silken wings in vain;   130
Or alum styptics[10] with contracting power
Shrink his thin essence like a riveled[11] flower:
Or, as Ixion[12] fixed, the wretch shall feel
The giddy motion of the whirling mill,
In fumes of burning chocolate shall glow,
And tremble at the sea that froths below!
    He spoke; the spirits from the sails descend;
Some, orb in orb, around the nymph extend;
Some thrid the mazy ringlets of her hair;
Some hang upon the pendants of her ear: 140
With beating hearts the dire event they wait,
Anxious, and trembling for the birth of fate.

---

[7] Earrings.
[8] From Latin *crispere*, meaning to cut.
[9] Needle with a large eye.
[10] Astringents.
[11] Shrivelled.
[12] In Greek myth Ixion was tortured in the underworld by being bound on an ever-turning wheel.

CANTO III

Close by those meads, forever crowned with flowers,
Where Thames with pride surveys his rising towers,
There stands a structure of majestic frame,
Which from the neighb'ring Hampton[1] takes its name.
Here Britain's statesmen oft the fall foredoom
Of foreign tyrants and of nymphs at home;
Here thou, great ANNA! whom three realms obey,[2]
Dost sometimes counsel take—and sometimes tea.
  Hither the heroes and the nymphs resort,
To taste awhile the pleasures of a court;   10
In various talk th' instructive hours they past,
Who gave the ball, or paid the visit last;
One speaks the glory of the British Queen,
And one describes a charming Indian screen;
A third interprets motions, looks, and eyes;
At every word a reputation dies.
Snuff, or the fan, supply each pause of chat,
With singing, laughing, ogling, *and all that.*
  Meanwhile, declining from the noon of day,
The sun obliquely shoots his burning ray;   20
The hungry judges soon the sentence sign,
And wretches hang that jury-men may dine;
The merchant from th' Exchange returns in peace,
And the long labors of the toilet cease.
Belinda now, whom thirst of fame invites,
Burns to encounter two advent'rous knights,
At ombre singly to decide their doom;
And swells her breast with conquests yet to come.
Straight the three bands prepare in arms to join,
Each band the number of the sacred nine.   30
Soon as she spreads her hand, th' aërial guard
Descend, and sit on each important card:
First Ariel perched upon a Matadore,[3]
Then each, according to the rank they bore;
For sylphs, yet mindful of their ancient race,

---

[1] Hampton Court Palace outside of London.
[2] Queen of England (1702-1714). The English maintained their foolish claim to rule France as well as Great Britain and Ireland.
[3] Matadors are the three cards of highest value in ombre. They are the Spadillio (ace of spades), Manillio (deuce of spades), Basto (the ace of clubs).

Are, as when women, wondrous fond of place.
  Behold, four Kings in majesty revered,
With hoary whiskers and a forky beard;
And four fair Queens whose hands sustain a flower,
Th' expressive emblem of their softer power;   40
Four Knaves in garbs succinct,[4] trusty band,
Caps on their heads, and halberts in their hand;
And particolored troops, a shining train,
Draw forth to combat on the velvet plain.
  The skilful nymph reviews her force with care:
Let Spades be trumps! she said, and trumps they were.
  Now move to war her sable Matadores,
In show like leaders of the swarthy Moors.
Spadillio first, unconquerable lord!
Led off two captive trumps, and swept the board.   50
As many more Manillio forced to yield,
And marched a victor from the verdant field.
Him Basto followed, but his fate more hard
Gained but one trump and one plebeian card.
With his broad sabre next, a chief in years,
The hoary Majesty of Spades appears,
Puts forth one manly leg, to sight revealed,
The rest, his many-colored robe concealed.
The rebel Knave, who dares his prince engage,
Proves the just victim of his royal rage.   60
Even mighty Pam,[5] that kings and queens o'erthrew
And mowed down armies in the fights of loo,
Sad chance of war! now destitute of aid,
Falls undistinguished by the victor spade!
  Thus far both armies to Belinda yield;
Now to the Baron fate inclines the field.
His warlike Amazon her host invades,
Th' imperial consort of the crown of Spades.
The Club's black tyrant first her victim died,
Spite of his haughty mien, and barb'rous pride: 70
What boots the regal circle on his head,
His giant limbs, in state unwieldy spread;
That long behind he trails his pompous robe,
And, of all monarchs, only grasps the globe?
  The Baron now his Diamonds pours apace;

---

4 Girded up.
5 The knave of clubs. It is the highest trump card in the game of loo.

Th' embroidered King who shows but half his face,
And his refulgent Queen, with powers combined
Of broken troops an easy conquest find.
Clubs, Diamonds, Hearts, in wild disorder seen,
With throngs promiscuous strow the level green.   80
Thus when dispersed a routed army runs,
Of Asia's troops, and Afric's sable sons,
With like confusion different nations fly,
Of various habit, and of various dye,
The pierced battalions of dis-united fall,
In heaps on heaps; one fate o'erwhelms them all.
   The Knave of Diamonds tries his wily arts,
And wins (oh shameful chance!) the Queen of Hearts.
At this, the blood the virgin's cheek forsook,
A livid paleness spreads o'er all her look;   90
She sees, and trembles at th' approaching ill,
Just in the jaws of ruin, and codille.⁶
And now (as oft in some distempered State)
On one nice Trick depends the general fate.
An Ace of Hearts steps forth: The King unseen
Lurked in her hand, and mourned his captive Queen:
He springs to vengeance with an eager pace,
And falls like thunder on the prostrate Ace.
The nymph exulting fills with shouts the sky;
The walls, the woods, and long canals reply.   100
   Oh thoughtless mortals! ever blind to fate,
Too soon dejected, and too soon elate.
Sudden, these honors shall be snatched away,
And cursed for ever this victorious day.
   For lo! the board with cups and spoons is crowned,
The berries crackle, and the mill turns round;⁷
On shining altars of Japan⁸ they raise
The silver lamp; the fiery spirits blaze:
From silver spouts the grateful liquors glide,
While China's earth receives the smoking tide: 110
At once they gratify their scent and taste,
And frequent cups prolong the rich repast.
Straight hover round the fair her airy band;
Some, as she sipped, the fuming liquor fanned,

---

⁶ Codille is the word signifying the main player's losing hand in the game of ombre.
⁷ Coffee is roasted and ground.
⁸ Lacquered tables.

Some o'er her lap their careful plumes displayed,
Trembling, and conscious of the rich brocade.
Coffee (which makes the politician wise,
And see through all things with his half-shut eyes)
Sent up in vapors to the Baron's brain
New stratagems, the radiant lock to gain.   120
Ah cease, rash youth! desist ere 'tis too late,
Fear the just Gods, and think of Scylla's fate!
Changed to a bird, and sent to flit in air,
She dearly pays for Nisus[9] injured hair!
  But when to mischief mortals bend their will,
How soon they find fit instruments of ill!
Just then, Clarissa drew with tempting grace
A two-edged weapon from her shining case:
So ladies in romance assist their knight,
Present the spear, and arm him for the fight.   130
He takes the gift with rev'rence, and extends
The little engine on his fingers' ends;
This just behind Belinda's neck he spread,
As o'er the fragrant steams she bends her head.
Swift to the lock a thousand sprites repair,
A thousand wings, by turns, blow back the hair;
And thrice they switched the diamond in her ear;
Thrice she looked back, and thrice the foe drew near.
Just in that instant, anxious Ariel sought
The close recesses of the virgin's thought;   140
As on the nosegay in her breast reclined,
He watched th' ideas rising in her mind,
Sudden he viewed, in spite of all her art,
An earthly lover lurking at her heart.
Amazed, confused, he found his power expired,
Resigned to fate, and with a sigh retired.
  The Peer now spreads the glitt'ring forfex[10] wide,
T' inclose the lock; now joins it, to divide.
Even then, before the fatal engine closed,
A wretched sylph too fondly interposed;   150
Fate urged the shears, and cut the sylph in twain,
(But airy substance soon unites again)

---

9 Scylla, daughter of Nisus, betrayed her father by cutting from his head a lock on which the whole kingdom depended and giving it to her lover, Minos. He was shocked at her deed and left her. She was turned into a bird.
  10 Scissors.

The meeting points the sacred hair dissever
From the fair head, forever, and forever!
  Then flashed the living lightning from her eyes,
And screams of horror rend th' affrighted skies.
Not louder shrieks to pitying heaven are cast,
When husbands, or when lap-dogs breathe their last;
Or when rich china vessels fall'n from high,
In glitt'ring dust and painted fragments lie!   160
Let wreaths of triumph now my temples twine,
(The victor cried) the glorious prize is mine!
While fish in streams, or birds delight in air,
Or in a coach and six the British fair,
As long as *Atalantis*[11] shall be read,
Or the small pillow grace a lady's bed,
While visits shall be paid on solemn days,
When num'rous wax-lights in bright order blaze,
While nymphs take treats, or assignations give,
So long my honor, name, and praise shall live!   170
What Time would spare, from steel receives its date,
And monuments, like men, submit to fate!
Steel could the labor of the Gods destroy,
And strike to dust th' imperial towers of Troy;
Steel could the works of mortal pride confound,
And hew triumphal arches to the ground.
What wonder then, fair nymph! thy hairs should feel,
The conq'ring force of unresisted steel?

CANTO IV

But anxious cares the pensive nymph oppressed,
And secret passions labored in her breast.
Not youthful kings in battle seized alive,
Not scornful virgins who their charms survive,
Not ardent lovers robbed of all their bliss,
Not ancient ladies when refused a kiss,
Not tyrants fierce that unrepenting die,
Not Cynthia[1] when her manteau's pinned awry,
E'er felt such rage, resentment, and despair,
As thou, sad virgin! for thy ravished hair.   10

---

[11] A notorious novel concerning contemporary court scandal written by Mrs. Manley (1709).
[1] Diana, goddess of the hunt and chastity. A manteau is a loose fitting robe.

For, that sad moment, when the sylphs withdrew
And Ariel weeping from Belinda flew,
Umbriel, a dusky, melancholy sprite,
As ever sullied the fair face of light,
Down to the central earth, his proper scene,
Repaired to search the gloomy Cave of Spleen.[2]
    Swift on his sooty pinions flits the gnome,
And in a vapour reached the dismal dome.
No cheerful breeze this sullen region knows,
The dreaded East is all the wind that blows.   20
Here in a grotto, sheltered close from air,
And screened in shades from day's detested glare,
She sighs forever on her pensive bed,
Pain at her side, and megrim[3] at her head.
    Two handmaids wait the throne: alike in place,
But diff'ring far in figure and in face.
Here stood Ill-nature like an ancient maid,
Her wrinkled form in black and white arrayed;
With store of prayers, for mornings, nights, and noons,
Her hand is filled; her bosom with lampoons.   30
    There Affectation, with a sickly mien,
Shows in her cheek the roses of eighteen,
Practised to lisp, and hang the head aside,
Faints into airs, and languishes with pride,
On the rich quilt sinks with becoming woe,
Wrapt in a gown, for sickness, and for show.
The fair ones feel such maladies as these,
When each new night-dress gives a new disease.
    A constant vapor[4] o'er the palace flies;
Strange phantoms rising as the mists arise;   40
Dreadful, as hermit's dreams in haunted shades,
Or bright, as visions of expiring maids.
Now glaring fiends, and snakes on rolling spires,
Pale specters, gaping tombs, and purple fires:
Now lakes of liquid gold, Elysian scenes,
And crystal domes, and angels in machines.[5]
    Unnumbered throngs on every side are seen,

---

[2] Ill humor.
[3] Headache.
[4] Referring to "The Vapors," the affectation of peevishness or petulance on the part of fashionable women.
[5] Mechanical devices used in the theater to create sensational stage effects.

Of bodies changed to various forms of Spleen.
Here living tea-pots stand, one arm held out,
One bent; the handle this, and that the spout: 50
A pipkin[6] there, like Homer's tripod walks;[7]
Here sighs a jar, and there a goose-pie talks,[8]
Men prove with child, as powerful fancy works,
And maids turned bottles, call aloud for corks.
    Safe past the gnome through this fantastic band,
A branch of healing spleenwort in his hand.
Then thus addressed the power: "Hail, wayward Queen!
Who rule the sex to fifty from fifteen:
Parent of vapors and of female wit,
Who give th' hysteric or poetic fit,   60
On various tempers act by various ways,
Make some take physic, others scribble plays;
Who cause the proud their visits to delay,
And send the godly in a pet to pray.
A nymph there is, that all thy power disdains,
And thousands more in equal mirth maintains.
But oh! if e'er thy gnome could spoil a grace,
Or raise a pimple on a beauteous face,
Like citron-waters[9] matrons' cheeks inflame,
Or change complexions at a losing game;   70
If e'er with airy horns I planted heads,[10]
Or rumpled petticoats, or tumbled beds,
Or caus'd suspicion when no soul was rude,
Or discomposed the head-dress of a prude,
Or e'er to costive[11] lap-dog gave disease,
Which not the tears of brightest eyes could ease:
Hear me, and touch Belinda with chagrin,
That single act gives half the world the spleen."
    The goddess with a discontented air
Seems to reject him, though she grants his prayer.   80
A wondrous bag with both her hands she binds,
Like that where once Ulysses held the winds;
There she collects the force of female lungs,
Sighs, sobs, and passions, and the war of tongues.

---

6 Earthen pot.
7 In the *Iliad* Vulcan provides mobile three-legged stools for the gods.
8 Pope noted that "a Lady of distinction imagin'd herself in this condition."
9 Flavored brandy.
10 I made men believe they had horns on their heads, that is, had unfaithful wives.
11 Constipated.

A vial next she fills with fainting fears,
Soft sorrows, melting griefs, and flowing tears.
The gnome rejoicing bears her gifts away,
Spreads his black wings and slowly mounts to day.
    Sunk in Thalestris'[12] arms the nymph he found,
Her eyes dejected and her hair unbound.   90
Full o'er their heads the swelling bag he rent,
And all the Furies issued at the vent.
Belinda burns with more than mortal ire,
And fierce Thalestris fans the rising fire.
"Oh wretched maid!" she spreads her hands, and cried,
(While Hampton's echoes, "Wretched maid!" replied)
"Was it for this you took such constant care
The bodkin, comb, and essence to prepare?
For this your locks in paper durance bound,
For this with torturing irons[13] wreathed around?   100
For this with fillets[14] trained your tender head,
And bravely bore the double loads of lead?
Gods! shall the ravisher display your hair,
While the fops envy, and the ladies stare!
Honor forbid! at whose unrivaled shrine
Ease, pleasure, virtue, all our sex resign.
Methinks already I your tears survey,
Already hear the horrid things they say,
Already see you a degraded toast,
And all your honor in a whisper lost!   110
How shall I, then, your helpless fame defend?
'Twill then be infamy to seem your friend!
And shall this prize, th' inestimable prize,
Exposed through crystal to the gazing eyes,
And heightened by the diamond's circling rays,
On that rapacious hand forever blaze?
Sooner shall grass in Hyde Park Circus grow,
And wits take lodgings in the sound of Bow,[15]
Sooner let earth, air, sea, to chaos fall,
Men, monkeys, lap-dogs, parrots, perish all!"   120
    She said; then raging to Sir Plume repairs,
And bids her beau demand the precious hairs:

---

12 The name stems from a queen of the Amazons and suggests one who is warlike.
13 Curlers with lead strips.
14 Bands for confining the hair somewhat like a hair net.
15 A district in London which was inhabited by merchants.

(Sir Plume of amber snuff-box justly vain,
And the nice conduct of a clouded cane)
With earnest eyes, and round unthinking face,
He first the snuff-box opened, then the case,
And thus broke out—"My Lord, why, what the devil?
Z—ds! damn the lock! 'fore Gad, you must be civil!
Plague on't! tis past a jest—nay prithee, pox!
Give her the hair"—he spoke, and rapped his box.   130
    "It grieves me much" (replied the Peer again)
"Who speaks so well should ever speak in vain.
But by this lock, this sacred lock I swear,
(Which never more shall join its parted hair;
Which never more its honors shall renew,
Clipped from the lovely head where late it grew)
That while my nostrils draw the vital air,
This hand, which won it, shall for ever wear."
He spoke, and speaking, in proud triumph spread
The long-contended honours of her head.   140
    But Umbriel, hateful gnome! forbears not so;
He breaks the vial whence the sorrows flow.
Then see! the nymph in beauteous grief appears,
Her eyes half-languishing, half-drowned in tears;
On her heaved bosom hung her drooping head,
Which, with a sigh, she raised; and thus she said.
    "Forever cursed be this detested day,
Which snatched my best, my fav'rite curl away!
Happy! ah ten times happy had I been,
If Hampton Court these eyes had never seen!   150
Yet am not I the first mistaken maid,
By love of courts to numerous ills betrayed.
Oh had I rather un-admired remained
In some lone isle, or distant Northern land;
Where the gilt chariot never marks the way,
Where none learn ombre, none e'er taste bohea![16]
There kept my charms concealed from mortal eye,
Like roses, that in deserts bloom and die.
What moved my mind with youthful lords to roam?
Oh had I stayed, and said my prayers at home!   160
'Twas this, the morning omens seemed to tell,
Thrice from my trembling hand the patch-box fell;

---

[16] Expensive tea.

The tott'ring china shook without a wind,
Nay, Poll sat mute, and Shock was most unkind!
A sylph too warned me of the threats of fate,
In mystic visions, now believed too late!
See the poor remnants of these slighted hairs!
My hands shall rend what even thy rapine spares:
These in two sable ringlets taught to break,
Once gave new beauties to the snowy neck; 170
The sister-lock now sits uncouth, alone,
And in its fellow's fate foresees its own;
Uncurled it hangs, the fatal shears demands,
And tempts once more, thy sacrilegious hands.
Oh hadst thou, cruel! been content to seize
Hairs less in sight, or any hairs but these!"

CANTO V

She said: the pitying audience melt in tears.
But Fate and Jove had stopped the Baron's ears.
In vain Thalestris with reproach assails,
For who can move when fair Belinda fails?
Not half so fixed the Trojan[1] could remain,
While Anna begged and Dido raged in vain.
Then grave Clarissa graceful waved her fan;
Silence ensued, and thus the nymph began.
  "Say why are beauties praised and honored most,
The wise man's passion, and the vain man's toast? 10
Why decked with all that land and sea afford,
Why angels called, and angel-like adored?
Why round our coaches crowd the white-gloved beaux,
Why bows the side-box from its inmost rows;
How vain are all these glories, all our pains,
Unless good sense preserve what beauty gains:
That men may say, when we the front-box grace:
'Behold the first in virtue as in face!'
Oh! if to dance all night, and dress all day,
Charmed the small-pox, or chased old-age away; 20
Who would not scorn what housewife's cares produce,
Or who would learn one earthly thing of use?

---

[1] In the *Aeneid* (IV. 9-34) Dido and her sister Anna beseech Aeneas not to leave
Carthage.

To patch, nay ogle, might become a saint,
Nor could it sure be such a sin to paint.
But since, alas! frail beauty must decay,
Curled or uncurled, since locks will turn to grey;
Since painted, or not painted, all shall fade,
And she who scorns a man, must die a maid;
What then remains but well our power to use,
And keep good-humor still whate'er we lose?   30
And trust me, dear! good-humor can prevail,
When airs, and flights, and screams, and scolding fail.
Beauties in vain their pretty eyes may roll;
Charms strike the sight, but merit wins the soul."
  So spoke the Dame, but no applause ensued;
Belinda frowned, Thalestris called her prude.
"To arms, to arms!" the fierce virago[2] cries,
And swift as lightning to the combat flies.
All side in parties, and begin th' attack;
Fans clap, silks rustle, and tough whalebones crack;   40
Heroes' and heroines' shouts confus'dly rise,
And bass and treble voices strike the skies.
No common weapons in their hands are found,
Like gods they fight, nor dread a mortal wound.
  So when bold Homer makes the gods engage,
And heavenly breasts with human passions rage;
'Gainst Pallas, Mars; Latona, Hermes arms;
And all Olympus rings with loud alarms:
Jove's thunder roars, heaven trembles all around,
Blue Neptune storms, the bellowing deeps resound: 50
Earth shakes her nodding towers, the ground gives way,
And the pale ghosts start at the flash of day!
  Triumphant Umbriel on a sconce's[3] height
Clapped his glad wings, and sat to view the fight:
Propped on their bodkin spears, the sprites survey
The growing combat, or assist the fray,
  While through the press enraged Thalestris flies,
And scatters death around from both her eyes.
A beau and witling perished in the throng,
One died in metaphor, and one in song.   60
"O cruel nymph! a living death I bear,"
Cried Dapperwit, and sunk beside his chair.

---

[2] A turbulent woman, a female warrior.
[3] Candlestick holder.

A mournful glance Sir Fopling upwards cast,
"Those eyes are made so killing"—was his last.
Thus on Maeander's flowery margin lies
Th' expiring swan, and as he sings he dies.
    When bold Sir Plume had drawn Clarissa down,
Chloe stepped in, and killed him with a frown;
She smiled to see the doughty hero slain,
But, at her smile, the beau revived again.   70
    Now Jove suspends his golden scales in air,
Weighs the men's wits against the lady's hair;
The doubtful beam long nods from side to side;
At length the wits mount up, the hairs subside.
    See, fierce Belinda on the Baron flies,
With more than usual lightning in her eyes:
Nor feared the chief th' unequal fight to try,
Who sought no more than on his foe to die.
    But this bold lord with manly strength endued,
She with one finger and a thumb subdued: 80
Just where the breath of life his nostrils drew,
A charge of snuff the wily virgin threw;
The gnomes direct, to every atom just,
The pungent grains of titillating dust.
Sudden, with starting tears each eye o'erflows,
And the high dome re-echoes to his nose.
    "Now meet thy fate," insensed Belinda cried,
And drew a deadly bodkin[4] from her side.
(The same, his ancient personage to deck,
Her great great grandsire wore about his neck,   90
In three seal-rings; which after, melted down,
Formed a vast buckle for his widow's gown:
Her infant grandame's whistle next it grew,
The bells she jingled, and the whistle blew;
Then in a bodkin graced her mother's hairs,
Which long she wore, and now Belinda wears.)
    "Boast not my fall" (he cried) "insulting foe!
Thou by some other shalt be laid as low,
Nor think, to die dejects my lofty mind:
All that I dread is leaving you behind!
Rather than so, ah let me still survive,
And burn in Cupid's flames—but burn alive."

---

[4] A pin shaped like a dagger.

"Restore the lock!" she cries; and all around,
"Restore the lock!" the vaulted roofs rebound.
Not fierce Othello in so loud a strain
Roared for the handkerchief that caused his pain.
But see how oft ambitious aims are crossed,
And chiefs contend till all the prize is lost!
The lock, obtained with guilt, and kept with pain,
In every place is sought, but sought in vain: 110
With such a prize no mortal must be blest,
So heaven decrees! with heaven who can contest?
    Some thought it mounted to the lunar sphere,
Since all things lost on earth are treasured there.
There heroes' wits are kept in pond'rous vases,
And beaux in snuff-boxes and tweezer-cases.
There broken vows and death-bed alms are found,
And lovers' hearts with ends of riband bound,
The courtier's promises, and sick man's prayers,
The smiles of harlots, and the tears of heirs,   120
Cages for gnats, and chains to yoke a flea,
Dried butterflies, and tomes of casuistry.[5]
    But trust the Muse—she saw it upward rise,
Though marked by none but quick, poetic eyes:
(So Rome's great founder[6] to the heavens withdrew,
To Proculus alone confessed in view)
A sudden star, it shot through liquid air,
And drew behind a radiant trail of hair.
Not Berenice's locks[7] first rose so bright,
The heavens bespangling with disheveled light.   130
The sylphs behold it kindling as it flies,
And pleased pursue its progress through the skies.
    This the beau monde[8] shall from the Mall[9] survey,
And hail with music its propitious ray.
This the blest lover shall for Venus take,
And send up vows from Rosamonda's lake.
This Partridge[10] soon shall view in cloudless skies,
When next he looks through Galileo's eyes;[11]

---

[5] Books of arguments concerning right and wrong conduct.
[6] Romulus.
[7] Berenice, the wife of Ptolemy III, gave a lock of her hair to the gods to ensure her husband's return from war and it turned into a constellation.
[8] The fashionable world.
[9] The Mall is a promenade in St. James' Park.
[10] A London astrologer often satirized for his ridiculous predictions.
[11] The telescope.

And hence th' egregious wizard shall foredoom
The fate of Louis, and the fall of Rome.   140
    Then cease, bright nymph! to mourn thy ravished hair,
Which adds new glory to the shining sphere!
Not all the tresses that fair head can boast,
Shall draw such envy as the lock you lost.
For, after all the murders of your eye,
When, after millions slain, yourself shall die:
When those fair suns shall set, as set they must,
And all those tresses shall be laid in dust,
This lock, the Muse shall consecrate to fame,
And 'midst the stars inscribe Belinda's name.   150

Questions for Discussion

1. Lord Petre, the Baron of the poem, cut off a lock of Miss Arabella Fermor's hair, which started a quarrel between the two families. *The Rape of the Lock* is a mock-epic based on this incident. What is Pope's attitude towards the subject—sarcastic, playful, or otherwise?

2. Is the guardian Sylph's speech in Canto I (lines 27-114) disproportionate in length? Why does Pope have him occupy so much of the first Canto?

3. In the boudoir scene Pope first calls Belinda a priestess and then a goddess as she peers in the mirror. Is he being inconsistent here?

4. In Canto II Belinda is compared to the sun (lines 1-14). What is the effect of the comparison—is it altogether flattering?

5. How seriously are we to take the guardian sylphs? Does Belinda know about them?

6. Pope's wit is often based on such incongruities as "lose her heart, or necklace, at a ball" (Canto II, line 109). Does this wit point to anything more than itself?

7. What is the function of lines 19-24 in Canto III where we momentarily look away from Belinda's world?

8. Is Belinda aggressive in the card game? Does she in any way deserve to lose her lock of hair?

9. Explain the satire on female vanity in Canto IV. In what way is "the cave of spleen" mock-heroic?

10. What is the function of the speech made by Belinda's friend Clarissa in Canto V (lines 9-34)?

11. Does the poem end happily for Belinda?

Jonathan Swift (1667-1745)

Description of a City Shower

Careful observers may fortell the Hour
(By sure Prognostics) when to dread a Show'r:
While Rain depends,[1] the pensive Cat gives o'er
Her Frolics, and pursues her Tail no more.
Returning Home at Night, you'll find the Sink[2]
Strike your offended Sense with double Stink.
If you be wise, then go not far to Dine;
You'll spend in Coach-hire more than save in Wine.
A coming Show'r your shooting Corns presage,
Old Aches throb, your hollow Tooth will rage.   10
Saunt'ring in Coffee-house is Dulman seen;
He damns the Climate, and complains of Spleen.[3]

Meanwhile the South, rising with dabbled Wings,
A sable Cloud athwart the Welkin flings,
That swill'd more Liquor than it could contain,
And like a Drunkard gives it up again.
Brisk Susan whips her Linen from the Rope,
While the first drizzling Show'r is born aslope,
Such is that Sprinkling which some careless Quean[4]
Flirts on you from her Mop, but not so clean.   20
You fly, invoke the Gods; then turning, stop
To rail; she, singing, still whirls on her Mop.
Not yet the Dust had shunn'd th' unequal Strife
But, aided by the Wind, fought still for Life;
And wafted with its Foe by violent Gust.
'Twas doubtful which was Rain, and which was Dust.
Ah! where must needy Poet seek for Aid,

---

[1] Is imminent.
[2] Sewer.
[3] Tendency toward melancholy.
[4] Slut.

When Dust and Rain at once his Coat invade,
His only Coat, where Dust, confus'd with Rain,
Roughen the Nap and leave a mingled Stain.   30

    Now in contiguous Drops the Flood comes down,
Threat'ning with Deluge this Devoted Town.
To Shops in Crowds the daggled[5] Females fly,
Pretend to cheapen Goods,[6] but nothing buy.
The Templer[7] spruce, while ev'ry Spout's a-broach,
Stays till 'tis fair, yet seems to call a Coach.
The tuck'd-up Sempstress walks with hasty Strides,
While Streams run down her oil'd Umbrella's Sides.
Here various Kinds of various Fortunes led
Commence Acquaintance underneath a Shed.   40
Triumphant Tories and desponding Whigs
Forget their Feuds, and join to save their Wigs.
    Box'd in a Chair[8] the Beau impatient sits,
While Spouts run clatt'ring o'er the Roof by Fits;
And ever and anon with frightful Din
The Leather sounds;[9] he trembles from within.
So when Troy Chair-men bore the Wooden Steed,
Pregnant with Greeks, impatient to be freed.
(Those Bully Greeks, who, as the Moderns do,
Instead of paying Chair-men, run them thro'.[10]   50
Laoco'n [11] struck the Outside with his Spear,
And each imprison'd Hero quak'd for Fear.

    Now from all Parts the swelling Kennels[12] flow,
And bear their Trophies with them as they go:
Filth of all Hues and Odours seem to tell
What Street they sail'd from, by their Sight and Smell.
They, as each Torrent drives, with rapid Force
From Smithfield, or St. Pulchre's shape their Course,
And in huge Confluent join at Snow-Hill Ridge.

---

[5] Splattered with mud.
[6] To bargain for goods.
[7] Law student.
[8] Sedan chair.
[9] The sedan chair's roof was made of leather.
[10] Run their swords through the chairmen.
[11] Trojan priest who hurled the spear at the Wooden Horse during the War of Troy. He was destroyed with his two sons by two huge serpents.
[12] Open gutters in the middle of the street.

Fall from the Conduit prone to Holborn-Bridge.[13]   60
Sweepings from Butchers' Stalls, Dung, Guts, and Blood,
Drown'd Puppies, stinking Sprats,[14] all drench'd in Mud.
Dead Cats and Turnip-Tops come tumbling down the Flood.

Questions for Discussion

1. Where does the satirical attitude first appear in the poem so that it is clear the poet is not simply describing a shower on a London street but is using it to expose moral failings among the inhabitants?

2. What particular social types is the poet satirizing? Why does he choose these particular ones to represent the moral failings of the city?

3. Why does the poet use so many ugly details in his satire? In what way do they suit his satire of the city?

4. What is the function of high-flown lines such as "A sable cloud athwart the welkin flings"? Is the comparison of the beau caught in his sedan chair to the Greeks in The Wooden Horse appropriate to the satirical intention of the poem? Why is the word *bully* used to describe the Greeks? Explain the mock-heroic tone of this scene.

5. Why is Swift so precise in naming various parts of the city from which the water is coming?

6. Can the flood at the end of the poem be compared to the Biblical flood? If so, how?

7. Whom is the speaker addressing and what tone does he use toward him?

---

[13] A description of the sewerage system of this section of London. Smithfield, center of cattle and sheep markets. Holborn Conduit, at the foot of Snow Hill, drained into Fleet Ditch at Holborn-Bridge, causing a great stench.

[14] Small herrings.

Jonathan Swift (1667-1745)

A Modest Proposal

FOR PREVENTING THE CHILDREN OF POOR PEOPLE IN IRE-
LAND FROM BEING A BURDEN TO THEIR PARENTS OR
COUNTRY, AND FOR MAKING THEM BENEFICIAL
TO THE PUBLIC

It is a melancholy object to those who walk through this great town[1] or travel in the country, when they see the streets, the roads, and cabin doors crowded with beggars of the female sex, followed by three, four, or six children, all in rags, and importuning every passenger for an alms. These mothers, instead of being able to work for their honest livelihood, are forced to employ all their time in strolling to beg sustenance for their helpless infants, who as they grow up, either turn thieves for want of work, or leave their dear native country, to fight for the Pretender in Spain,[2] or sell themselves to the Barbadoes.[3]

I think it is agreed by all parties, that this prodigious number of children in the arms, or on the backs, or at the heels of their mothers, and frequently of their fathers, is in the present deplorable state of the kingdom a very great additional grievance; and therefore whoever could find out a fair, cheap, and easy method of making these children sound and useful members of the common-wealth, would deserve so well of the public as to have his statue set up for a preserver of the nation.

But my intention is very far from being confined to provide only for the children of professed beggars; it is of a much greater extent, and shall take in the whole number of infants at a certain age, who are born of par-

---

[1] Dublin.

[2] The Pretender is James Francis Edward Stuart (1688-1766), son of King James II, who claimed the throne of England after his father was deposed during the Bloodless Revolution of 1688. His followers, known as Jacobites, were involved in an intrigue with the Spanish prime minister.

[3] They become indentured servants in Barbadoes, a British colony in the West Indies.

ents in effect as little able to support them, as those who demand our charity in the streets.

As to my own part, having turned my thoughts, for many years, upon this important subject, and maturely weighed the several schemes of other projectors,[4] I have always found them grossly mistaken in their computation. It is true, a child just dropt from its dam may be supported by her milk for a solar year with little other nourishment, at most not above the value of two shillings, which the mother may certainly get, or the value in scraps, by her lawful occupation of begging; and it is exactly at one year old that I propose to provide for them in such a manner, as, instead of being a charge upon their parents, or the parish, or wanting food and raiment for the rest of their lives, they shall, on the contrary, contribute to the feeding and partly to the clothing of many thousands.

There is likewise another great advantage in my scheme, that it will prevent those voluntary abortions, and that horrid practice of women murdering their bastard children, alas! too frequent among us—sacrificing the poor innocent babes, I doubt, more to avoid the expense than the shame—which would move tears and pity in the most savage and inhuman breast.

The number of souls in this kingdom[5] being usually reckoned one million and a half, of these I calculate there may be about two hundred thousand couples whose wives are breeders; from which number I subtract thirty thousand couples, who are able to maintain their own children, although I apprehend there cannot be so many, under the present distresses of the kingdom; but this being granted, there will remain an hundred and seventy thousand breeders. I again subtract fifty thousand, for those women who miscarry, or whose children die by accident or disease within the year. There only remain an hundred and twenty thousand children of poor parents annually born: The question therefore is, How this number shall be reared, and provided for? which, as I have already said, under the present situation of affairs, is utterly impossible by all the methods hitherto proposed; for we can neither employ them in handicraft or agriculture; we neither build houses, (I mean in the country) nor cultivate land: They can very seldom pick up a livelihood by stealing till they arrive at six years old, except where they are of towardly parts, although, I confess, they learn the rudiments much earlier; during which time they can however be properly looked upon only as probationers; as I have been informed by a principal gentleman in the county of Cavan, who protested to me, that he never knew above one or two instances under the age of six, even in a part of the kingdom so renowned for the quickest proficiency in that art.

I am assured by our merchants, that a boy or girl before twelve years old, is no saleable commodity, and even when they come to this age, they

---

[4] Devisers of schemes.
[5] Ireland.

will not yield above three pounds, or three pounds and half a crown at most, on the exchange; which cannot turn to account either to the parents or kingdom, the charge of nutrient and rags having been at least four times that value.

I shall now therefore humbly propose my own thoughts, which I hope will not be liable to the least objection.

I have been assured by a very knowing American of my acquaintance in London, that a young healthy child well nursed is at a year old a most delicious nourishing and wholesome food, whether stewed, roasted, baked, or boiled; and I make no doubt that it will equally serve in a fricassee, or a ragout.[6]

I do therefore humbly offer it to publick consideration, that of the hundred and twenty thousand children, already computed, twenty thousand may be reserved for breed, whereof only one fourth part to be males; which is more than we allow to sheep, black cattle, or swine; and my reason is that these children are seldom the fruits of marriage, a circumstance not much regarded by our savages; therefore one male will be sufficient to serve four females. That the remaining hundred thousand may, at a year old, be offered in sale to the persons of quality and fortune through the kingdom; always advising the mother to let them suck plentifully in the last month, so as to render them plump and fat for a good table. A child will make two dishes at an entertainment for friends; and when the family dines alone, the fore or hind quarter will make a reasonable dish, and seasoned with a little pepper or salt will be very good boiled on the fourth day, especially in winter.

I have reckoned upon a medium that a child just born will weigh twelve pounds, and in a solar year, if tolerably nursed, increaseth to twenty-eight pounds.

I grant this food will be somewhat dear, and therefore very proper for landlords, who, as they have already devoured most of the parents, seem to have the best title to the children.

Infant's flesh will be in season throughout the year, but more plentiful in March, and a little before and after; for we are told by a grave author, an eminent French physician,[7] that fish being a prolific diet, There are more children born in Roman Catholic countries about nine months after Lent, than at any other season; therefore, reckoning a year after Lent, the markets will be more glutted than usual because the number of popish infants is at least three to one in this kingdom, and therefore it will have one other collateral advantage, by lessening the number of papists among us.

I have already computed the charge of nursing a beggar's child (in which list I reckon all cottagers, laborers, and four-fifths of the farmers)

[6] Meat stew.
[7] François Rabelais (ca. 1494-1553). He was a writer of comedy and satire.

to be about two shillings per annum, rags included; and I belive no gentle-man would repine to give ten shillings for the carcass of a good fat child, which, as I have said, will make four dishes of excellent nutritive meat, when he hath only some particular friend or his own family to dine with him. Thus the squire will learn to be a good landlord, and grow popular among his tenants; the mother will have eight shillings net profit, and be fit for work till she produces another child.

Those who are more thrifty (as I must confess the times require) may flay the carcass, the skin of which, artificially[8] dressed, will make admirable gloves for ladies, and summer boots for fine gentlemen.

As to our city of Dublin, shambles[9] may be appointed for this purpose in the most convenient parts of it, and butchers we may be assured will not be wanting; although I rather recommend buying the children alive and dressing them hot from the knife, as we do roasting pigs.

A very worthy person, a true lover of his country, and whose virtues I highly esteem, was lately pleased in discoursing on this matter to offer a refinement upon my scheme. He said that many gentlemen of this king-dom, having of late destroyed their deer, he conceived that the want of venison might be well supplied by the bodies of young lads and maidens, not exceeding fourteen years of age nor under twelve; so great a number of both sexes in every country being now ready to starve for want of work and service; and these to be disposed of by their parents if alive, or otherwise by their nearest relations. But with due deference to so excellent a friend, and so deserving a patriot, I cannot be altogether in his sentiments; for as to the males, my American acquaintance assured me from frequent experi-ence that their flesh was generally tough and lean, like that of our school-boys, by continual exercise, and their taste disagreeable; and to fatten them would not answer the charge. Then as to the females, it would, I think with humble submission, be a loss to the publick, because they soon would be-come breeders themselves: and besides it is not improbable that some scrupulous people might be apt to censure such a practice (although indeed very unjustly) as a little bordering upon cruelty, which, I confess, hath always been with me the strongest objection against any project, how well soever intended.

But in order to justify my friend, he confessed that this expedient was put into his head by the famous Psalmanazar,[10] a native of the island Formosa, who came from thence to London, above twenty years ago, and in con-versation told my friend that in his country when any young person hap-

---

8 Skillfully.

9 Slaughterhouses.

10 George Psalmanazar (ca. 1679-1763) was a Frenchman who wrote a fictitious account of Formosa and was considered an imposter.

pened to be put to death, the executioner sold the carcass to persons of quality, as a prime dainty, and that, in his time, the body of a plump girl of fifteen, who was crucified for an attempt to poison the Emperor, was sold to his Imperial Majesty's prime minister of state, and other great mandarins of the court, in joints from the gibbet, at four hundred crowns. Neither indeed can I deny, that if the same use were made of several plump young girls in this town, who, without one single groat to their fortunes, cannot stir abroad without a chair, and appear at a play-house and assemblies in foreign fineries which they never will pay for, the kingdom would not be the worse.

Some persons of a desponding spirit are in great concern about that vast number of poor people, who are aged, diseased, or maimed, and I have been desired to employ my thoughts what course may be taken, to ease the nation of so grievous an encumbrance. But I am not in the least pain upon that matter, because it is very well known, that they are every day dying, and rotting, by cold, and famine, and filth, and vermin, as fast as can be reasonably expected. And as to the younger laborers, they are now in almost as hopeful a condition. They cannot get work, and consequently pine away for want of nourishment, to a degree, that if at any time they are accidentally hired to common labour, they have not strength to perform it, and thus the country and themselves are happily delivered from the evils to come.

I have too long digressed, and therefore shall return to my subject. I think the advantages by the proposal which I have made are obvious and many, as well as of the highest importance.

For *first*, as I have already observed, it would greatly lessen the number of Papists, with whom we are yearly over-run, being the principal breeders of the nation, as well as our most dangerous enemies, and who stay at home on purpose with a design to deliver the kingdom to the Pretender, hoping to take their advantage by the absence of so many good Protestants, who have chosen rather to leave their country, than stay at home, and pay tithes against their conscience to an Episcopal curate.

Secondly, the poorer tenants will have something valuable of their own, which by law may be made liable to distress[11] and help to pay their landlord's rent, their corn and cattle being already seized, and money a thing unknown.

Thirdly, whereas the maintenance of an hundred thousand children, from two years old and upward, cannot be computed at less than ten shillings apiece per annum, the nation's stock will be thereby increased fifty thousand pounds per annum, besides the profit of a new dish introduced to the tables of all gentlemen of fortune in the kingodm who have any refinement in

---

11 The seizure of goods or property for the payment of debts or other obligations.

taste. And the money will circulate among ourselves, the goods being entirely of our own growth and manufacture.

Fourthly, the constant breeders, beside the gain of eight shillings sterling per annum by the sale of their children, will be rid of the charge of maintaining them after the first year.

Fifthly, this food would likewise bring great custom to taverns, where the vintners will certainly be so prudent as to produce the best receipts for dressing it to perfection, and consequently have their houses frequented by all the fine gentlemen who justly value themselves upon their knowledge in good eating; and a skillful cook, who understands how to oblige his guests, will contrive to make it as expensive as they please.

Sixthly, this would be a great inducement to marriage, which all wise nations have either encouraged by rewards or enforced by laws and penalties. It would increase the care and the tenderness of mothers toward their children, when they were sure of a settlement for life to the poor babes, provided in some sort by the public, to their annual profit instead of expense. We should soon see an honest emulation among the married women, which of them could bring the fattest child to the market. Men would become as fond of their wives during the time of their pregnancy as they are now of their mares in foal, their cows in calf, their sows when they are ready to farrow; nor offer to beat or kick them (as is too frequent a practice) for fear of a miscarriage.

Many other advantages might be enumerated. For instance, the addition of some thousand carcasses in our exportation of barreled beef, the propagation of swine's flesh, and improvement in the art of making good bacon, so much wanted among us by the great destruction of pigs too frequent at our tables; which are no way comparable in taste or magnificence to a well-grown, fat, yearling child, which roasted whole will make a considerable figure at a lord mayor's feast or any other public entertainment. But this and many others I omit, being studious of brevity.

Supposing that one thousand families in this city would be constant customers for infants' flesh, besides others who might have it at merry meetings, particularly at weddings and christenings, I compute that Dublin would take off annually about twenty thousand carcasses; and the rest of the kingdom (where probably they will be sold somewhat cheaper) the remaining eighty thousand.

I can think of no one objection that will possibly be raised against this proposal, unless it should be urged that the number of people will be thereby much lessened in the kingdom. This I freely own, and 'twas indeed one principal design in offering it to the world. I desire the reader will observe that I calculate my remedy for this one individual kingdom of Ireland, and for no other that ever was, is, or, I think, ever can be upon earth. Therefore let no man talk to me of other expedients: of taxing our absentees at five shillings a pound; of using neither clothes, nor household furniture, except what is of our own growth and manufacture; of utterly rejecting the materials and instruments that promote foreign luxury; of curing the expensiveness of pride, vanity, idleness, and gaming in our women; of introducing a vein of parsimony, prudence and temperance; of learning to love our country, wherein we differ from Laplanders, and the inhabitants of Topinamboo;[12] of quitting our animosities, and factions, nor act any longer like the Jews, who were murdering one another at the very moment their city was taken;[13] of being a little cautious not to sell our country and consciences for nothing; of teaching landlords to have at least one degree of mercy towards their tenants; lastly, of putting a spirit of honesty, industry, and skill into our shopkeepers, who, if a resolution could now be taken to buy only our native goods, would immediately unite to cheat and exact upon us in the price, the measure, and the goodness, nor could ever yet be brought to make one fair proposal of just dealing, though often and earnestly invited to it.

Therefore I repeat, let no man talk to me of these and the like expedients, till he hath at least some glimpse of hope, that there will ever be some hearty and sincere attempt to put them in practice.

But as to my self, having been wearied out for many years with offering vain, idle, visionary thoughts, and at length utterly despairing of success, I fortunately fell upon this proposal, which as it is wholly new, so it hath something solid and real, of no expense and little trouble, full in our own power, and whereby we can incur no danger in disobliging England. For this kind of commodity will not bear exportation, the flesh being of too tender a consistence, to admit a long continuance in salt, although perhaps I could name a country,[14] which would be glad to eat up our whole nation without it.

After all, I am not so violently bent upon my own opinion as to reject any offer proposed by wise men, which shall be found equally innocent, cheap, easy, and effectual. But before something of that kind shall be advanced in contradiction to my scheme, and offering a better, I desire the author or authors will be pleased maturely to consider two points. First, as things now stand, how they will able to find food and raiment for a hundred thousand useless mouths and backs. And secondly, there being a round million of creatures in human figure throughout this kingdom, whose whole subsistence put into a common stock would leave them in debt two

---

12 The Laplanders love their cold country and the savages of Brazil their jungles more than the English in Ireland love that country.

13 The siege of Jerusalem by the Romans in A.D. 70.

14 England.

millions of pounds sterling, adding those who are beggars by profession, to the bulk of farmers, cottagers and labourers, with their wives and children, who are beggars in effect; I desire those politicians, who dislike my overture, and may perhaps be so bold to attempt an answer, that they will first ask the parents of these mortals, whether they would not at this day think it a great happiness to have been sold for food at a year old, in the manner I prescribe, and thereby have avoided such a perpetual scene of misfortunes as they have since gone through, by the oppression of landlords, the impossibility of paying rent without money or trade, the want of common sustenance, with neither house nor clothes to cover them from the inclemencies of the weather, and the most inevitable prospect of entailing the like or greater miseries upon their breed for ever.

I profess, in the sincerity of my heart, that I have not the least personal interest in endeavoring to promote this necessary work, having no other motive than the public good of my country, by advancing our trade, providing for infants, relieving the poor, and giving some pleasure to the rich. I have no children by which I can propose to get a single penny; the youngest being nine years old, and my wife past child-bearing.

Questions for Discussion

1. Characterize the speaker of the essay and indicate what social group he is addressing.

2. Why is the matter-of-fact tone appropriate for the essay?

3. To what extent is this situation a fictional one? How is it related to the actual situation in Ireland?

4. What is the moral position which Swift upholds? What practical suggestions does he make for alleviating conditions in Ireland?

5. Compare this satire with Juvenal's, and discuss indirect ways in which Swift and Juvenal approach their subjects.

Voltaire (1694-1778)

Candide or the Optimist

ADAPTED FROM THE TRANSLATION BY WILLIAM F. FLEMING

Chapter I.

HOW CANDIDE WAS BROUGHT UP IN A MAGNIFICENT
CASTLE AND HOW HE WAS DRIVEN FROM THERE.

In the country of Westphalia, in the castle of the baron of Thunder-ten-tronckh, lived a youth whom nature had endowed with a most sweet disposition. His face was the true index of his mind. He had a solid judgment joined to the most unaffected simplicity; and hence, I presume, he had his name of Candide. The old servants of the house suspected him to have been the son of the baron's sister, by a very good sort of a gentleman of the neighborhood, whom that young lady refused to marry, because he could produce no more than seventy-one quarterings in his arms;[1] the rest of the genealogical tree belonging to the family having been lost through the injuries of time.

The baron was one of the most powerful lords in Westphalia; for his castle had not only a gate, but even windows; and his great hall was hung with tapestry. He used to hunt with his mastiffs and spaniels instead of greyhounds; his groom served him for huntsman; and the parson of the parish officiated as his grand almoner[2] He was called My Lord by all his people, and he never told a story but every one laughed at it.

My lady baroness weighed three hundred and fifty pounds, consequently was a person of no small consideration; and then she did the honors of the house with a dignity that commanded universal respect. Her daughter was about seventeen years of age, fresh colored, comely, plump, and desirable. The baron's son seemed to be a youth in every respect worthy of the father

---

[1] Divisions on a coat of arms to indicate the degrees of nobility.
[2] Distributor of alms at the court.

he sprung from. Pangloss, the tutor, was the oracle of the family, and little Candide listened to his instructions with all the simplicity natural to his age and disposition.

Master Pangloss[3] taught metaphysico-theologo-cosmolo-nigology.[4] He could prove to admiration that there is no effect without a cause; and, that in this best of all possible worlds, the baron's castle was the most magnificent of all castles, and my lady the best of all possible baronesses.

It is demonstrable, said he, that things cannot be otherwise than as they are; for as all things have been created for some end, they must necessarily be created for the best end. Observe, for instance, the nose is formed for spectacles, therefore we wear spectacles. The legs are visibly designed for stockings, accordingly we wear stockings. Stones were made to be hewn, and to construct castles, therefore My Lord has a magnificent castle; for the greatest baron in the province ought to be the best lodged. Swine were intended to be eaten, therefore we eat pork all the year round: and they, who assert that everything is *right*, do not express themselves correctly; they should say that everything is *best*.

Candide listened attentively, and believed implicitly; for he thought Cunégonde excessively handsome, though he never had the courage to tell her so. He concluded that next to the happiness of being baron of Thunder-ten-tronckh, the next was that of being Cunégonde, the next that of seeing her every day, and the last that of hearing the doctrine of Master Pangloss, the greatest philosopher of the whole province, and consequently of the whole world.

One day when Cunégonde went to take a walk in a little neighboring wood which was called a park, she saw, through the bushes, the sage Doctor Pangloss giving a lecture in experimental philosophy to her mother's chambermaid, a little brown wench, very pretty, and very tractable. As Cunégonde had a great disposition for the sciences, she observed with the utmost attention the experiments, which were repeated before her eyes; she perfectly well understood the force of the doctor's reasoning upon causes and effects. She retired greatly flurried, quite pensive and filled with the desire of knowledge, imagining that she might be a *sufficient reason* for young Candide, and he for her.

On her way back, she happened to meet the young man; she blushed, he blushed also; she wished him a good morning in a flattering tone, he returned the salute, without knowing what he said. The next day, as they were rising from dinner, Cunégonde and Candide slipped behind the screen. She dropped her handkerchief, the young man picked it up. She innocently took

---

[3] The word means literally "all-tongue."

[4] A caricature of the philosophy of Leibnitz (1646-1716) whose ideas were made popular by Alexander Pope in his *Essay on Man* and Christian Wolff (1679-1754).

hold of his hand, and he as innocently kissed hers with a warmth, a sensibility, a grace—all very particular; their lips met; their eyes sparkled; their knees trembled; their hands strayed. The baron chanced to come by; he beheld the cause and effect, and, without hesitation, saluted Candide with some notable kicks in the behind, and drove him out of doors. Cunégonde fainted away, and, as soon as she came to herself, the baroness boxed her ears. Thus a general consternation was spread over this most magnificent and most agreeable of all possible castles.

Chapter II.

WHAT BEFELL CANDIDE AMONG THE BULGARIANS.

Candide, thus driven out of this terrestrial paradise, rambled a long time without knowing where he went; sometimes he raised his eyes, all bedewed with tears, towards heaven, and sometimes he cast a melancholy look towards the magnificent castle, where dwelt the fairest of young baronesses. He laid himself down to sleep in a furrow, heartbroken, and supperless. The snow fell in great flakes, and, in the morning when he awoke, he was almost frozen to death; however, he crawled to the next town, which was called Wald-berghoff-trarbkdikdorff, without a penny in his pocket, and half dead with hunger and fatigue. He took up his stand at the door of an inn. He had not been long there, before two men dressed in blue, fixed their eyes steadfastly upon him. "Comrade," said one of them to the other, "yonder is a well made young fellow, and of the right size." Upon which they made up to Candide, and with the greatest civility and politeness invited him to dine with them. "Gentlemen," replied Candide, with a most engaging modesty, "you do me much honor, but upon my word I have no money." "Money, sir!" said one of the blues to him, "young persons of your appearance and merit never pay anything; why, are not you five feet five inches high?" "Yes, gentlemen, that is really my size," replied he, with a low bow. "Come then, sir, sit down along with us; we will not only pay your reckoning, but will never suffer such a clever young fellow as you to want money. Men were born to assist one another." "You are perfectly right, gentlemen," said Candide, "this is precisely the doctrine of Master Pangloss; and I am convinced that everything is for the best." His generous companions next entreated him to accept a few crowns, which he readily complied with, at the same time offering them his note for the payment, which they refused, and sat down to table. "Have you not a great affection for—" "O yes! I have a great affection for the lovely Cunégonde." "May be so," replied one of the blues, "but that is not the question! We ask you whether you have not a great affection for the king of the Bulgarians?"[1] "For the king of the Bulgarians?" said Candide, "oh Lord! not at all, why I never saw him in my life." "Is it possible! oh, he is a most charming king! Come, we must drink his health." "With all my heart, gentlemen," says Candide, and off he tossed his glass. "Bravo!" cry the blues; "you are now the support, the defender, the hero of the Bulgarians; your fortune is made; you are in the high road to glory." So saying, they handcuffed him, and carried him away to the regiment. There he was made to wheel about to the right, to the left, to draw his ramrod, to return his ramrod, to present, to fire, to march, and they gave him thirty blows with a cane; the next day he performed his exercise a little better, and they gave him but twenty; the day following he came off with ten, and was looked upon as a young fellow of surprising genius by all his comrades.

Candide was struck with amazement, and could not conceive how he came to be a hero. One fine spring morning he took it into his head to take a walk, and he marched straight forward, conceiving it to be a privilege of the human species, as well as of the brute creation, to make use of their legs how and when they pleased. He had not gone above two leagues when he was overtaken by four other heroes, six feet high, who bound him neck and heels, and carried him to a dungeon. A court-martial sat upon him, and he was asked which he liked better, to run the gauntlet thirty-six times through the whole regiment, or to have his brains blown out with a dozen musket-balls? In vain did he remonstrate to them that the human will is free, and that he chose neither; they obliged him to make a choice, and he determined, in virtue of that divine gift called free will, to run the gauntlet thirty-six times. He had gone through this discipline twice, and the regiment being composed of 2,000 men, they composed for him exactly 4,000 strokes, which laid bare all his muscles and nerves from the nape of his neck to his stern. As they were preparing to make him set out the third time, our young hero, unable to support it any longer, begged as a favor that they would be so obliging as to shoot him through the head; the favor being granted, a bandage was tied over his eyes, and he was made to kneel down. At that very instant, his Bulgarian majesty happening to pass by made a stop, and inquired into the delinquent's crime, and being a prince of great penetration, he found, from what he heard of Candide, that he was a young metaphysician, entirely ignorant of the world; and therefore, out of his great clemency, he condescended to pardon him, for which his name will be celebrated in every journal, and in every age. A skilful surgeon cured Candide in three weeks by means of emollients prescribed by Dioscorides.[2] His sores were now

---

[1] Frederick the Great of Prussia whom Voltaire visited in 1750.

[2] Greek physician of the first century A. D.

skinned over and he was able to march, when the king of the Bulgarians gave battle to the king of the Abarians.[3]

Chapter III.

HOW CANDIDE ESCAPED FROM THE BULGARIANS, AND WHAT BEFELL HIM AFTERWARDS.

Never was anything so gallant, so well turned out, so brilliant, and so finely disposed as the two armies. The trumpets, fifes, oboes, drums, and cannon made such harmony as never was heard in hell itself. The entertainment began by a discharge of cannon, which, in the twinkling of an eye, laid flat about six thousand men on each side. The musket bullets swept away, out of the best of all possible worlds, nine or ten thousand scoundrels that infested its surface. The bayonet was next the sufficient reason of the deaths of several thousands. The whole might amount to thirty thousand souls. Candide trembled like a philosopher, and concealed himself as well as he could during this heroic butchery.

At length, while the two kings were causing *Te Deums* to be sung in their camps, Candide took a resolution to go and reason somewhere else upon causes and effects. After passing over heaps of dead or dying men, the first place he came to was a neighboring village, in the Abarian territories, which had been burned to the ground by the Bulgarians, according to the laws of war. Here lay a number of old men covered with wounds, who beheld their wives dying with their throats cut, and hugging their children to their breasts, all stained with blood. There several young virgins, whose bodies had been ripped open, after they had satisfied the natural necessities of the Bulgarian heroes, breathed their last; while others, half burned in the flames, begged to be despatched out of the world. The ground about them was covered with the brains, arms, and legs of dead men.

Candide made all the haste he could to another village, which belonged to the Bulgarians, and there he found the heroic Abares had enacted the same tragedy. Continuing to walk over palpitating limbs, or through ruined buildings, at length he arrived beyond the theatre of war, with a little provision in his budget, and Cunégonde's image in his heart. When he arrived in Holland his provision failed him; but having heard that the inhabitants of that country were all rich and Christians, he made himself sure of being treated by them in the same manner as at the baron's castle, before he had been driven from there through the power of Cunégonde's bright eyes.

---

3 The French, who fought the Prussians in the Seven Years' War (1756-1763).

He asked charity of several grave-looking people, who one and all answered him, that if he continued to follow this trade they would have him sent to the house of correction, where he should be taught to get his bread.

He next addressed himself to a person who had just come from haranguing a numerous assembly for a whole hour on the subject of charity. The orator, squinting at him under his broad-brimmed hat, asked him sternly, what brought him thither and whether he was for the good old cause? "Sir," said Candide, in a submissive manner, "I conceive there can be no effect without a cause; everything is linked together by necessity and arranged for the best. It was necessary that I should be banished from the presence of Cunégonde; that I should afterwards run the gauntlet; and it is necessary I should beg my bread, till I am able to get it: all this could not have been otherwise." "Friend," said the orator, "do you hold the pope to be Antichrist?" "Truly, I never heard anything about it," said Candide, "but whether he is or not, I am in want of something to eat." "You deserve neither to eat nor to drink," replied the orator, "wretch, monster, that you are! hence! avoid my sight, nor ever come near me again while you live." The orator's wife happened to put her head out of the window at that instant, when, seeing a man who doubted whether the pope was Antichrist, she discharged upon his head a pot full of . . . Good heavens, to what excess does religious zeal transport womankind!

A man who had never been christened, an honest Anabaptist named James, was witness to the cruel and ignominious treatment showed to one of his brethren, to a rational being with two feet and no wings. Moved with pity he carried him to his own house, washed him, gave him meat and drink, and made him a present of two florins, at the same time proposing to instruct him in his own trade of weaving Persian silks, which are fabricated in Holland. Candide, filled with so much goodness, threw himself at his feet, crying, "Now I am convinced that my Master Pangloss told me truth when he said that everything was for the best in this world; for I am infinitely more affected with your extraordinary generosity than with the inhumanity of that gentleman in the black cloak, and his wife." The next day, as Candide was walking out, he met a beggar all covered with scabs, his eyes sunk in his head, the end of his nose eaten off, his mouth drawn on one side, his teeth as black as a cloak, snuffling and coughing most violently, and every time he attempted to spit dropping a tooth.

[In Chapter 4, Candide discovers that the beggar is Pangloss. The Bulgarians, he tells Candide, assaulted Cunégonde and the other members of the family and destroyed the castle. Pangloss has contracted a disease from

Paquette, the Baroness' maid, but he insists that the malady is "indispensable in this best of worlds." Candide, Pangloss, and Jacques sail for Lisbon; they arrive as a storm and an earthquake begin.]

Chapter V.

A TEMPEST, A SHIPWRECK, AN EARTHQUAKE; AND
WHAT ELSE BEFELL DR. PANGLOSS, CANDIDE, AND
JAMES THE ANABAPTIST.

Half the passengers, weakened and half-dead with the inconceivable anxiety and sickness which the rolling of a vessel at sea occasions through the whole human frame, were lost to all sense of the danger that surrounded them. The others made loud outcries, or went to their prayers; the sails were blown into shreds, and the masts were brought by the board. The vessel was a total wreck. Every one was busily employed, but nobody could be either heard or obeyed. The anabaptist, being upon deck, lent a helping hand as well as the rest, when a brutish sailor gave him a blow and laid him speechless; but, with the violence of the blow the sailor himself tumbled headlong overboard, and fell upon a piece of the broken mast, which he immediately grasped. Honest James, forgetting the injury he had so lately received from him, flew to his assistance, and, with great difficulty, hauled him in again, but, in the attempt, was, by a sudden jerk of the ship, thrown overboard himself, in sight of the very fellow whom he had risked his life to save, and who took not the least notice of him in this distress. Candide, who beheld all that passed and saw his benefactor one moment rising above water, and the next swallowed up by the merciless waves, was preparing to jump after him, but was prevented by the philosopher Pangloss, who demonstrated to him that the roadstead of Lisbon had been made on pur- pose for the Anabaptist to be drowned there. While he was proving his argument *a priori*, the ship foundered, and the whole crew perished, except Pangloss, Candide, and the sailor who had been the means of drowning the good Anabaptist. The villain swam ashore; but Pangloss and Candide reached the land upon a plank.

As soon as they had recovered from their surprise and fatigue they walked towards Lisbon; with what little money they had left they thought to save themselves from starving after having escaped drowning.

Scarcely had they ceased to lament the loss of their benefactor and set foot in the city, when they perceived that the earth trembled under their feet, and the sea, swelling and foaming in the harbor, was dashing in pieces the vessels that were riding at anchor. Large sheets of flames and cinders covered the streets and public places; the houses tottered, and were tumbled topsy-turvy even to their foundations, which were themselves destroyed, and thirty thousand inhabitants of both sexes, young and old, were buried beneath the ruins.[1] The sailor, whistling and swearing, cried, "Damn it, there's something to be got here." "What can be the *sufficient reason* for this phenomenon?" said Pangloss. "It is certainly the day of judgment," said Candide. The sailor, defying death in the pursuit of plunder, rushed into the midst of the ruin, where he found some money, with which he got drunk, and, after he had slept himself sober he purchased the favors of the first good-natured wench that came in his way, amidst the ruins of demolished houses and the groans of half-buried and expiring persons. Pangloss pulled him by the sleeve; "Friend," said he, "this is not right, you trespass against the *universal reason,* and have mistaken your time." "Death and zounds!" answered the other, "I am a sailor and was born at Batavia, and have trampled four times upon the crucifix in as many voyages to Japan;[2] you have come to a good hand with your *universal reason.*"

In the meantime, Candide, who had been wounded by some pieces of stone that fell from the houses, lay stretched in the street, almost covered with rubbish. "For God's sake," said he to Pangloss, "get me a little wine and oil! I am dying." "This concussion of the earth is no new thing," said Pangloss, "the city of Lima in South America, experienced the same last year; the same cause, the same effects; there is certainly a train of sulphur all the way underground from Lima to Lisbon. "Nothing is more probable," said Candide; "but for the love of God a little oil and wine." "Probable!" replied the philosopher, "I maintain that the thing is demonstrable." Candide fainted away, and Pangloss fetched him some water from a neighboring spring.

The next day, in searching among the ruins, they found something to eat with which they replenished their exhausted strength. After this they assisted the inhabitants in relieving the distressed and wounded. Some, whom they had humanely assisted, gave them as good a dinner as could be expected under such terrible circumstances. The repast, indeed, was mournful, and the company moistened their bread with their tears; but Pangloss endeavored to comfort them under this affliction by affirming that things

---

[1] The Lisbon earthquake occurred on November 1, 1775. It provoked Voltaire into satirizing the doctrine of optimism held by Leibnitz. In a letter on the disaster Voltaire wrote: "One will find it difficult to divine how the laws of motion bring about such terrible disasters in *the best of all possible worlds.*" Leibnitz's philosophy was an attempt "to reconcile a mechanistic interpretation of the universe with belief in a God whose ends are just and good."

[2] The Japanese forced Europeans trading with them to perform this sacrilegious act in order to discourage Christians from doing business in Japan.

could not be otherwise than they were: "For," said he, "all this is for the very best end, for if there is a volcano at Lisbon it could be in no other spot; and it is impossible but things should be as they are, for everything is for the best."

By the side of the tutor sat a little man dressed in black, who was one of the *familiars*[3] of the Inquisition. This person, taking him up with great complaisance, said, "Possibly, my good sir, you do not believe in original sin; for, if everything is best, there could have been no such thing as the fall or punishment of man."

"I humbly ask your excellency's pardon," answered Pangloss, still more politely; "for the fall of man and the curse consequent thereupon necessarily entered into the system of the best of worlds." "That is as much as to say, sir," rejoined the *familiar*, "you do not believe in free will." "Your excellency will be so good as to excuse me," said Pangloss, "free will is consistent with absolute necessity; for it was necessary we should be free, for in that the will—"

Pangloss was in the midst of his proposition, when the inquisitor beckoned to his attendant to help him to a glass of port wine.

Chapter VI.

HOW THE PORTUGUESE MADE A SUPERB AUTO-DA-FÉ
TO PREVENT ANY FUTURE EARTHQUAKES, AND
HOW CANDIDE UNDERWENT PUBLIC
FLAGELLATION

After the earthquake, which had destroyed three-fourths of the city of Lisbon, the sages of that country could think of no means more effectual to preserve the kingdom from utter ruin than to entertain the people with an *auto-da-fé*,[1] it having been decided by the University of Coimbra that the burning of a few people alive by a slow fire, and with great ceremony, is an infallible preventive of earthquakes.

In consequence thereof they had seized on a Biscayan for marrying his godmother, and on two Portuguese for taking out the bacon of a chicken they were eating;[2] after dinner they came and secured Doctor Pangloss, and his pupil Candide, the one for speaking his mind, and the other for

---

[3] Officers of the Inquisition.

[1] "Act of faith." Reference to a sentence imposed by the Inquisition that resulted in the burning of a heretic at the stake.

[2] An indication they were still faithful to Judaism.

seeming to approve what he had said. They were conducted to separate apartments, extremely cool, where they were never uncomfortable with the sun. Eight days afterwards they were each dressed in a *sanbenito*, and their heads were adorned with paper mitres. The mitre and *sanbenito*[3] worn by Candide were painted with flames reversed and with devils that had neither tails nor claws; but Doctor Pangloss's devils had both tails and claws, and his flames were upright. In these habits they marched in procession, and heard a very pathetic sermon, which was followed by an anthem, accompanied by bagpipes. Candide was flogged to some tune, while the anthem was being sung; the Biscayan and the two men who would not eat bacon were burned, and Pangloss was hanged, which is not a common custom at these solemnities. The same day there was another earthquake, which made most dreadful havoc.

Candide, amazed, terrified, confounded, astonished, all bloody, and trembling from head to foot, said to himself, "If this is the best of all possible worlds what are the others? If I had only been whipped, I could have put up with it, as I did among the Bulgarians; but oh my dear Pangloss! my beloved master! you greatest of philosophers! that ever I should live to see you hanged, without knowing for what! O my dear Anabaptist, you best of men, that it should be your fate to be drowned in the very harbor! O Cunégonde, you mirror of young ladies! that it should be your fate to have your body ripped open!"

He was making the best of his way from the place where he had been preached to, whipped, absolved and blessed, when he was accosted by an old woman, who said to him: "Take courage, child, and follow me."

[In Chapter 7, a strange old woman takes care of Candide. She brings him to Cunégonde, who tells him that she has survived being raped and disembowelled.]

Chapter VIII.

CUNÉGONDE'S STORY.

"I was in bed, and fast asleep, when it pleased heaven to send the Bulgarians to our delightful castle of Thunder-ten-tronckh, where they murdered

---

[3] The robe of a heretic condemned to die by the Inquisition.

my father and brother, and cut my mother in pieces. A tall Bulgarian soldier, six feet high, perceiving that I had fainted away at this sight, attempted to ravish me; the operation brought me to my senses. I cried, I struggled, I bit, I scratched, I would have torn the tall Bulgarian's eyes out, not knowing that what had happened at my father's castle was a customary thing. The brutal soldier, enraged at my resistance, gave me a wound in my left leg with his dagger, the mark of which I still carry." "I long to see it," said Candide, with all imaginable simplicity. "You shall," said Cunégonde, "but let me proceed." "Pray do," replied Candide.

She continued. "A Bulgarian captain came in, and saw me weltering in my blood, and the soldier still as busy as if no one had been present. The officer, enraged at the fellow's want of respect to him, killed him with one stroke of his sabre as he lay upon me. This captain took care of me, had me cured, and carried me as a prisoner of war to his quarters. I washed what little linen he possessed, and cooked his victuals: he was very fond of me, that was certain; neither can I deny that he was well made, and had a soft, white skin, but he was very stupid, and knew nothing of philosophy: it might plainly be perceived that he had not been educated under Doctor Pangloss. In three months, having gambled away all his money, and having grown tired of me, he sold me to a Jew, named Don Issachar, who traded in Holland and Portugal, and was passionately fond of women. This Jew showed me great kindness, in hopes of gaining favors; but he never could prevail on me to yield. A modest woman may be once ravished; but her virtue is greatly strengthened thereby. In order to make sure of me, he brought me to this country-house you now see. I had hitherto believed that nothing could equal the beauty of the castle of Thunder-ten-tronckh; but I found I was mistaken.

"The Grand Inquisitor saw me one day at Mass, eyed me all through the service, and when it was over, sent to let me know he wanted to speak with me about some private business. I was conducted to his palace, where I told him all my story; he represented to me how much it was beneath a person of my birth to belong to a circumcised Israelite. He caused a proposal to be made to Don Issachar, that he should resign me to his lordship. Don Issachar, being the court banker, and a man of credit, was not easy to be prevailed upon. His lordship threatend him with an *auto-da-fé;* in short, my Jew was frightened into a compromise, and it was agreed between them, that the house and myself should belong to both in common; that the Jew should have Monday, Wednesday, and the Sabbath to himself; and the inquisitor the other four days of the week. This agreement has subsisted almost six months; but not without several contests, whether the space from Saturday night to Sunday morning belonged to the old or the new law.

For my part, I have hitherto withstood them both, and truly I believe this is the very reason why they are both so fond of me.

"At length to turn aside the scourge of earthquakes, and to intimidate Don Issachar, my lord inquisitor was pleased to celebrate an *auto-da-fé.* He did me the honor to invite me to the ceremony. I had a very good seat; and refreshments of all kinds were offered the ladies between mass and the execution. I was dreadfully shocked at the burning of the two Jews, and the honest Biscayan who married his godmother; but how great was my surprise, my consternation, and concern, when I beheld a figure so like Pangloss, dressed in a *sanbenito* and mitre! I rubbed my eyes, I looked at him attentively. I saw him hanged, and I fainted away: scarce had I recovered my senses, when I saw you stripped of clothing; this was the height of horror, grief, and despair. I must confess to you for a truth, that your skin is whiter and more blooming that that of the Bulgarian captain. This spectacle worked me up to a pitch of distraction. I screamed out, and would have said, 'hold, barbarians!' but my voice failed me; and indeed my cries would have signified nothing. After you had been severely whipped, how is it possible, I said to myself, that the lovely Candide and the sage Pangloss should be at Lisbon, the one to receive a hundred lashes, and the other to be hanged by order of my lord inquisitor, of whom I am so great a favorite? Pangloss deceived me most cruelly, in saying that everything is for the best.

"Thus agitated and perplexed, now distracted and lost, now half dead with grief, I revolved in my mind the murder of my father, mother, and brother, committed before my eyes; the insolence of the rascally Bulgarian soldier; the wound he gave me in the groin; my servitude; my being a cook-wench to my Bulgarian captain; my subjection to the hateful Jew, and my cruel inquisitor; the hanging of Doctor Pangloss; the *Miserere* sung while you were being whipped; and particularly the kiss I gave you behind the screen, the last day I ever beheld you. I returned thanks to God for having brought you to the place where I was, after so many trials. I charged the old woman who attends me to bring you here as soon as was convenient. She has punctually executed my orders, and I now enjoy the inexpressible satisfaction of seeing you, hearing you, and speaking to you. But you must certainly be half-dead with hunger; I myself have a great inclination to eat, and so let us sit down to supper."

Upon this the two lovers immediately placed themselves at table, and, after having supped, they returned to seat themselves again on the magnificent sofa already mentioned, when Señor Don Issachar, one of the masters of the house, entered unexpectedly; it was the Sabbath day, and he came to enjoy his privilege, and sigh forth his passion at the feet of the fair Cunégonde.

[In Chapter 9, Candide kills Don Issachar, but in self-defense. Soon the Inquisitor enters and Candide likewise kills him. Candide, Cunégonde, and the old woman escape to Avecena in the mountains.]

Chapter X.

IN WHAT DISTRESS CANDIDE, CUNÉGONDE, AND THE OLD WOMAN ARRIVE AT CADIZ; AND OF THEIR EMBARKATION.

"Who could it be that has robbed me of my gold coins and jewels?" exclaimed Cunégonde, all bathed in tears. "How shall we live? What shall we do? Where shall I find inquisitors and Jews who can give me more?" "Alas!" said the old woman, "I have a shrewd suspicion of a reverend father, who lay last night in the same inn with us at Badajoz; God forbid I should condemn any one wrongfully, but he came into our room twice, and he set off in the morning long before us." "Alas!" said Candide, "Pangloss has often demonstrated to me that the goods of this world are common to all men, and that everyone has an equal right to the enjoyment of them; but, according to these principles, the father ought to have left us enough to carry us to the end of our journey. Have you nothing at all left, my dear Cunégonde?" "Not a maravedi," replied she. "What is to be done then?" said Candide. "Sell one of the horses," replied the old woman, "I will get up behind Cunégonde, though I have only one cushion to ride on, and we shall reach Cadiz."

In the same inn there was a Benedictine friar, who bought the horse very cheap. Candide, Cunégonde, and the old woman, after passing through Lucina, Chellas, and Lebrixa, arrived at length at Cadiz. A fleet was then getting ready, and troops were assembling in order to induce the reverend fathers, Jesuits of Paraguay, who were accused of having excited one of the Indian tribes in the neighborhood of the town of the Holy Sacrament, to revolt against the kings of Spain and Portugal. Candide, having been in the Bulgarian service, performed the military exercise of that nation before the general of this little army with so intrepid an air, and with such agility and expedition, that he received the command of a company of infantry. Being now made a captain, he embarked with Cunégonde, the old woman, two valets, and the two Andalusian horses, which had belonged to the Grand Inquisitor of Portugal.

During their voyage they amused themselves with many profound reasonings on poor Pangloss's philosophy. "We are now going into another world, and surely it must be there that everything is for the best; for I must confess that we have had some little reason to complain of what passes in ours, both as to the physical and moral part. Though I have a sincere love for you," said Cunégonde, "yet I still shudder at the reflection of what I have seen and experienced." "All will be well," replied Candide, "the sea of this new world is already better than our European seas: it is smoother, and the winds blow more regularly." "God grant it," said Cunégonde, "but I have met with such terrible treatment in this world that I have almost lost all hopes of a better one." Cried the old woman: "If you had suffered half what I have, there might be some reason for complaining." Cunégonde could scarce refrain from laughing at the good old woman, and thought it droll enough to pretend to a greater share of misfortunes than her own. "Alas! my good dame," said she, "unless you had been ravished by two Bulgarians, had received two deep wounds in your belly, had seen two of your own castles demolished, had lost two fathers, and two mothers, and seen both of them barbarously murdered before your eyes, and to sum up all, had two lovers whipped at an *auto-da-fé*, I cannot see how you could be more unfortunate than I. Add to this, though born a baroness, and bearing seventy-two quarterings, I have been reduced to the station of a cook-wench." "Miss," replied the old woman, "you do not know my family as yet; but if I were to show you my posteriors, you would not talk in this manner, but suspend your judgment." This speech raised an extreme curiosity in Candide and Cunégonde; and the old woman continued as follows:

Chapter XI.

THE HISTORY OF THE OLD WOMAN.

"I have not always been blear-eyed. My nose did not always touch my chin; nor was I always a servant. You must know that I am the daughter of Pope Urban X,[1] and of the princess of Palestrina. To the age of fourteen I was brought up in a castle, compared with which all the castles of the German barons would not have been fit for stabling, and one of my robes would have bought half the province of Westphalia. I grew up, and improved in beauty, wit, and every graceful accomplishment; and in the

---

[1] Voltaire's posthumous note: "Behold the author's extreme discretion. Up to now there has never been a Pope called Urban X. The author fears to present a known Pope with a bastard daughter. What circumspection! What delicacy of conscience."

midst of pleasures, homage, and the highest expectations. I already began to inspire the men with love. My breast began to take its right form, and such a breast! white, firm, and formed like that of Venus of Medici; my eyebrows were as black as jet, and as for my eyes, they darted flames and eclipsed the lustre of the stars, as I was told by the poets of our part of the world. My maids, when they dressed and undressed me, used to fall into an ecstasy in viewing me before and behind: and all the men longed to be in their places.

"I was contracted in marriage to a sovereign prince of Massa Carara. Such a prince! as handsome as myself, sweet-tempered, agreeable, witty, and in love with me over head and ears. I loved him, too, as our sex generally do for the first time, with rapture and idolatry. The nupitals were prepared with surprising pomp and magnificence; the ceremony was attended with feasts, tournaments, and comic operas: all Italy composed sonnets in my praise, though not one of them was tolerable. I was on the point of reaching the summit of bliss, when an old marchioness, who had been mistress to the prince, my husband, invited him to drink chocolate. In less than two hours after he returned from the visit, he died of most terrible convulsions. But this is a mere trifle. My mother, distracted to the highest degree, and yet less afflicted than I, determined to leave for some time so fatal a place. As she had a very fine estate in the neighborhood of Gaeta, we embarked on board a galley, which was gilded like the high altar of St. Peter's, at Rome. In our passage we were boarded by a Salé rover. Our men defended themselves like true Pope's soldiers; they flung themselves upon their knees, laid down their arms, and begged the corsair to give them absolution *in articulo mortis.*[2]

"The Moors presently stripped us as bare as ever we were born. My mother, my maids of honor, and myself, were treated in the same manner. It is amazing how quick these gentry are at undressing people. But what surprised me most was, that they made a rude sort of surgical examination of parts of the body which are sacred to the functions of nature. I thought it a very strange kind of ceremony; for thus we are generally apt to judge of things when we have not seen the world. I afterwards learned that it was to discover if we had any diamonds concealed. This practice has been established since time immemorial among those civilized nations that scour the seas. I was informed that the religious knights of Malta never fail to make this search whenever any Moors of either sex fall into their hands. It is a part of the law of nations, from which they never deviate.

"I need not tell you how great a hardship it was for a young princess and her mother to be made slaves and carried to Morocco. You may easily im-

---

2 At the point of death.

agine what we must have suffered on board a corsair. My mother was still extremely handsome, our maids of honor, and even our common waiting-women, had more charms than were to be found in all Africa. As for my-self, I was enchanting; I was beauty itself, and then I had my virginity. But, alas! I did not retain it long; this precious flower, which had been reserved for the lovely prince of Massa Carara, was cropped by the captain of the Moorish vessel, who was a hideous negro, and thought he did me infinite honor. Indeed, both the princess of Palestrina and I must have had very strong constitutions to undergo all the hardships and violences we suffered before our arrival at Morocco. But I will not detain you any longer with such common things; they are hardly worth mentioning.

"Upon our arrival at Morocco we found that kingdom deluged with blood. Fifty sons of the emperor Muley Ishmael were each at the head of a party. This produced fifty civil wars of blacks against blacks, of tawnies against tawnies, and of mulattoes against mulattoes. In short, the whole empire was one continual scene of carnage.

"No sooner were we landed than a party of blacks, of a contrary faction to that of my captain, came to rob him of his booty. Next to the money and jewels, we were the most valuable things he had. I witnessed on this occasion such a battle as you never beheld in your cold European climates. The northern nations have not that fermentation in their blood, nor that raging lust for women that is so common in Africa. The natives of Europe seem to have their veins filled with milk only; but fire and vitriol circulate in those of the inhabitants of Mount Atlas and the neighboring provinces. They fought with the fury of the lions, tigers, and serpents of their country, to decide who should have us. A Moor seized my mother by the right arm, while my captain's lieutenant held her by the left; another Moor laid hold of her by the right leg, and one of our corsairs led her by the other. In this manner almost all of our women were dragged by four soldiers. My captain kept me concealed behind him, and with his drawn scimitar cut down every-one who opposed him; at length I saw all our Italian women and my mother mangled and torn in pieces by the monsters who contended for them. The captives, my companions, the Moors who took us, the soldiers, the sailors, the blacks, the whites, the mulattoes, and lastly, my captain himself, were all slain, and I remained alone expiring upon a heap of dead bodies. Similar barbarous scenes were transacted every day over the whole country, which is of three hundred leagues in extent, and yet they never missed the five stated times of prayer enjoined by their prophet Mahomet.

"I disengaged myself with great difficulty from such a heap of corpses, and made a shift to crawl to a large orange-tree that stood on the bank of a neighboring rivulet, where I fell down exhausted with fatigue, and over-whelmed with horror, despair, and hunger. My senses being overpowered,

I fell asleep, or rather seemed to be in a trance. Thus I lay in a state of weakness and insensibility between life and death, when I felt myself pressed by something that moved up and down upon my body. This brought me to myself. I opened my eyes, and saw a fair-faced man, who sighed and muttered these words between his teeth, *O che sciagura d'essere senza coglioni!*[3]

Chapter XII.

THE ADVENTURES OF THE OLD WOMAN CONTINUED.

"Astonished and delighted to hear my native language, and no less surprised at the young man's words, I told him that there were far greater misfortunes in the world than what he complained of. And to convince him of it, I gave him a short history of the horrible disasters that had happened to me; and as soon as I had finished, fell into a swoon again. He carried me in his arms to a neighboring cottage, where he had me put to bed, procured me something to eat, waited on me with the greatest attention, comforted me, caressed me, told me that he had never seen anything so perfectly beautiful as myself, and that he had never so much regretted the loss of what no one could restore to him. 'I was born at Naples,' said he, 'where they make eunuchs of thousands of children every year; some die of the operation; some acquire voices far beyond the most tuneful of your ladies; and others are sent to govern states and empires. I underwent this operation very successfully, and was one of the singers in the princess of Palestrina's chapel.' 'How,' cried I, 'in my mother's chapel!' 'The princess of Palestrina, your mother!' cried he, bursting into a flood of tears. 'Is it possible you should be the beautiful young princess whom I had the care of bringing up till she was six years old, and who at that tender age promised to be as fair as I now behold you?' 'I am the same,' I replied. 'My mother lies about a hundred yards from here cut in pieces and buried under a heap of dead bodies.'

"I then related to him all that had happened to me, and he in return acquainted me with all his adventures, and how he had been sent to the court of the king of Morocco by a Christian prince to conclude a treaty with that monarch; in consequence of which he was to be furnished with military stores, and ships to enable him to destroy the commerce of other Christian governments. 'I have executed my commission,' said the eunuch; 'I am going to take ship at Ceuta, and I'll take you along with me to Italy. *Ma che sciagura d'essere senza coglioni!*'

---

3 "Oh, what an affliction to be a eunuch!"

"I thanked him with tears of joy, but, instead of taking me with him into Italy, he carried me to Algiers, and sold me to the dey[1] of that province. I had not been long a slave when the plague, which had made the tour of Africa, Asia, and Europe, broke out at Algiers with redoubled fury. You have seen an earthquake; but tell me, Miss, have you ever had the plague?"

"Never," answered the young baroness.

"If you had ever had it," continued the old woman, "you would own an earthquake was a trifle to it. It is very common in Africa; I was seized with it. Figure to yourself the distressed condition of the daughter of a pope, only fifteen years old, and who in less than three months had felt the miseries of poverty and slavery; had been debauched almost every day; had beheld her mother cut into four quarters; had experienced the scourges of famine and war; and was now dying of the plague at Algiers. I did not, however, die of it; but my eunuch, and the dey, and almost the whole seraglio of Algiers, were swept off.

"As soon as the first fury of this dreadful pestilence was over, a sale was made of the dey's slaves. I was purchased by a merchant who carried me to Tunis. This man sold me to another merchant, who sold me again to another at Tripoli; from Tripoli I was sold to Alexandria, from Alexandria to Smyrna, and from Smyrna to Constantinople. After many changes, I at length became the property of an aga of the janizaries,[2] who, soon after I came into his possession, was ordered away to the defence of Azoff, then besieged by the Russians.

"The aga, being very fond of women, took his whole seraglio with him, and lodged us in a small fort, with two black eunuchs and twenty soldiers for our guard. Our army made a great slaughter among the Russians; but they soon returned us the compliment. Azoff[3] was taken by storm, and the enemy spared neither age, sex, nor condition, but put all to the sword, and laid the city in ashes. Our little fort alone held out; they resolved to reduce us by famine. The twenty janissaries, who were left to defend it, had bound themselves by an oath never to surrender the place. Being reduced to the extremity of famine, they found themselves obliged to kill our two eunuchs, and eat them rather than violate their oath. But this horrible repast soon failing them, they next determined to devour the women.

"We had a very pious and humane man, who gave them a most excellent sermon on this occasion, exhorting them not to kill us all at once. 'Cut off only one of the steaks of each of those ladies,' said he, 'and you will fare extremely well; if you are under the necessity of having recourse to the

---

[1] Governor.

[2] Bodyguards of the Turkish Sultan.

[3] The sea of Azov.

same expedient again, you will find the like supply a few days hence. Heaven will approve of so charitable an action, and work your deliverance.'

"By the force of this eloquence he easily persuaded them, and all of us underwent the operation. The man applied the same balsam as they do to children after circumcision. We were all ready to give up the ghost.

"The janissaries had scarcely time to finish the repast with which we had supplied them, when the Russians attacked the place by means of flat-bottomed boats, and not a single janizary escaped. The Russians paid no regard to the condition we were in; but there are French surgeons in all parts of the world, and one of them took us under his care, and cured us. I shall never forget, while I live, that as soon as my wounds were perfectly healed he made me certain proposals. In general, he desired us all to be of good cheer, assuring us that the like had happened in many sieges; and that it was perfectly agreeable to the laws of war.

"As soon as my companions were in a condition to walk, they were sent to Moscow. As for me, I fell to the lot of a boyar,[4] who put me to work in his garden, and gave me twenty lashes a day. But this nobleman having about two years afterwards been broken alive upon the wheel, with about thirty others, for some court intrigues, I took advantage of the event, and made my escape. I travelled over a great part of Russia. I was a long time an inn-keeper's servant at Riga, then at Rostock, Wismar, Leipzig, Cassel, Utrecht, Leyden, The Hague, and Rotterdam: I have grown old in misery and disgrace living with only one buttock, and having in perpetual remembrance that I am a Pope's daughter. I have been a hundred times upon the point of killing myself, but still I was fond of life. This ridiculous weakness is, perhaps, one of the dangerous principles implanted in our nature. For what can be more absurd than to persist in carrying a burden of which we wish to be eased? to detest, and yet to strive to preserve our existence? In a word, to caress the serpent that devours us, and hug him close to our bosoms till he has gnawed into our hearts?

"In the different countries which it has been my fate to traverse, and at the many inns where I have been a servant, I have observed a prodigious number of people who held their existence in abhorrence, and yet I never knew more than twelve who voluntarily put an end to their misery; namely, three Negroes, four Englishmen, as many Genevese, and a German professor, named Robek.[5] My last place was with a Jew, Don Issachar, who placed me near your person, my fair lady; to whose fortunes I have attached myself, and have been more concerned with your adventures than with my own. I should never have even mentioned the latter to you, had you not a

---

[4] Russian nobleman.
[5] He wrote a defense of suicide and drowned himself at the age of sixty-seven.

little piqued me on the head of sufferings; and if it was not customary to tell stories on board a ship in order to pass away the time. In short, my dear Miss, I have a great deal of knowledge and experience in the world; therefore take my advice: divert yourself, and prevail upon each passenger to tell his story, and if there is one of them all that has not cursed his existence many times, and said to himself over and over again that he was the most wretched of mortals, I give you leave to throw me head long into the sea."

[In Chapter 13, after their arrival at Buenos Aires they call on the governor. He proposes to Cunégonde and the old woman tells her to accept. Candide must leave, because it is known that he killed the Inquisitor.]

Chapter XIV.

THE RECEPTION CANDIDE AND CACAMBO MET WITH AMONG THE JESUITS IN PARAGUAY.

Candide had brought with him from Cadiz such a footman as one often meets with on the coasts of Spain and in the colonies. He was the fourth part of a Spaniard, of a mongrel breed, and born in Tucuman.[1] He had successively gone through the profession of a singing boy, sexton, sailor, monk, peddler, soldier, and lackey. His name was Cacambo; he had a great affection for his master, because his master was a very good man. He immediately saddled the two Andalusian horses. "Come, my good master, let us follow the old woman's advice, and make all the haste we can from this place without staying to look behind us." Candide burst into a flood of tears: "O, my dear Cunégonde, must I then be compelled to quit you just as the governor was going to honor us with his presence at our wedding! Cunégonde, so long lost and found again, what will now become of you?" "Lord!" said Cacambo, "she must do as well as she can; women are never at a loss. God takes care of them, and so let us make the best of our way." "But where will you carry me? where can we go? what can we do without Cunégonde?" cried the disconsolate Candide. "By St. James of Compostella," said Cacambo, "you were going to fight against the Jesuits of Paraguay; now let us go and fight for them; I know the road perfectly well; I'll conduct you to their kingdom; they will be delighted with a captain that understands the Bulgarian drill; you will certainly make a prodigious fortune.

---

[1] Argentine province.

If we cannot succeed in this world we may in another. It is a great pleasure to see new objects and perform new exploits."

"Then you have been in Paraguay?" asked Candide. "Indeed I have," replied Cacambo; "I was a servant in the college of the Assumption, and am as well acquainted with the new government of Los Padres[2] as I am with the streets of Cadiz. Oh, it is an admirable government, that is most certain! The kingdom is at present upwards of three hundred leagues in diameter, and divided into thirty provinces; the fathers there are masters of everything, and the people have no money at all; this you must allow is the masterpiece of justice and reason. For my part, I see nothing so divine as the good fathers, who wage war in this part of the world against the troops of Spain and Portugal, at the same time that they hear the confessions of those very princes in Europe; who kill Spaniards in America and send them to heaven in Madrid. This pleases me exceedingly, but let us push forward; you are going to see the happiest and most fortunate of all mortals. How charmed will those fathers be to hear that a captain who understands the Bulgarian military drill is coming among them."

As soon as they reached the first barrier, Cacambo called to the advance guard, and told them that a captain wanted to speak to my lord, the general. Notice was given to the main guard, and immediately a Paraguayan officer ran to throw himself at the feet of the commandant to impart this news to him. Candide and Cacambo were immediately disarmed, and their two Andalusian horses were seized. The two strangers were conducted between two files of musketeers, the commandant was at the further end with a three-cornered cap on his head, his gown tucked up, a sword by his side, and a half-pike in his hand; he made a sign, and instantly twenty-four soldiers drew up round the newcomers. A sergeant told them that they must wait, the commandant could not speak to them; and that the reverend father provincial did not suffer any Spaniard to open his mouth but in his presence, or to stay above three hours in the province. "And where is the reverend father provincial?" said Cacambo. "He has just come from Mass and is at the parade," replied the sergeant, "and in about three hours' time you may possibly have the honor to kiss his spurs." "But," said Cacambo, "the captain, who, as well as myself, is perishing of hunger, is no Spaniard, but a German; therefore, pray, might we not be permitted to break our fast till we can be introduced to his reverence?"

The sergeant immediately went and acquainted the commandant with what he heard. "God be praised," said the reverend commandant, "since he is a German I will hear what he has to say; let him be brought to my arbor."

Immediately they conducted Candide to a beautiful pavilion adorned with a colonade of green marble, spotted with yellow, and with an intertexture of

---

[2] The Jesuits.

vines, which served as a kind of cage for parrots, humming-birds, guinea-hens, and all other curious kinds of birds. An excellent breakfast was provided in vessels of gold; and while the Paraguayans were eating coarse Indian corn out of wooden dishes in the open air, and exposed to the burning heat of the sun, the reverend father commandant retired to his cool arbor.

He was a very handsome young man, round-faced, fair, and fresh-colored, his eyebrows were finely arched, he had a piercing eye, the tips of his ears were red, his lips vermilion, and he had a bold and commanding air; but such a boldness as neither resembled that of a Spaniard nor of a Jesuit. He ordered his men to give back to Candide and Cacambo their arms, together with their two Andalusian horses. Cacambo gave the poor beasts some oats to eat close by the arbor, keeping a strict eye upon them all the while for fear of surprise.

Candide having kissed the hem of the commandant's robe, they sat down to table. "It seems you are a German," said the Jesuit to him in that language. "Yes, reverend father," answered Candide. As they pronounced these words they looked at each other with great amazement and with an emotion that neither could conceal.

"From what part of Germany do you come?" said the Jesuit.

"From the dirty province of Westphalia," answered Candide. "I was born in the castle of Thunder-ten-tronckh."

"Oh heavens! is it possible?" said the commandant.

"What a miracle!" cried Candide.

"Can it be you?" said the commandant.

On this they both drew a few steps backwards, then running into each other's arms, embraced, and wept profusely. "Is it you then, reverend father? You are the brother of the fair Cunégonde? You who were slain by the Bulgarians! You the baron's son! You a Jesuit in Paraguay! I must confess this is a strange world we live in. O Pangloss! Pangloss! what joy this would have given you if you had not been hanged."

The commandant dismissed the Negro slaves, and the Paraguayans who presented them with liquor in crystal goblets. He returned thanks to God and St. Ignatius[3] a thousand times; he clasped Candide in his arms, and both their faces were bathed in tears. "You will be more surprised, more affected, more excited," said Candide, "when I tell you that Cunégonde, your sister, whose belly was supposed to have been ripped open, is in perfect health."

"Where?"

"In your neighborhood, with the governor of Buenos Aires; and I myself was going to fight against you." Every word they uttered during this long conversation was productive of some new matter of astonishment. Their

---

[3] St. Ignatius Loyola founded the Jesuit order.

souls fluttered on their tongues, listened in their ears, and sparkled in their eyes. Like true Germans, they continued a long while at table, waiting for the reverend father; and the commandant spoke to his dear Candide as follows:

Chapter XV.

HOW CANDIDE KILLED THE BROTHER OF HIS DEAR CUNÉGONDE.

"Never while I live shall I lose the memory of that horrible day on which I saw my father and mother barbarously butchered before my eyes, and my sister ravished. When the Bulgarians retired we searched in vain for my dear sister. She was nowhere to be found; but the bodies of my father, mother, and myself, with two servant maids and three little boys, all of whom had been murdered by the remorseless enemy, were thrown into a cart to be buried in a chapel belonging to the Jesuits, within two leagues of our family seat. A Jesuit sprinkled us with some holy water, which was very salty, and a few drops of it went into my eyes; the father perceived that my eyelids stirred a little; he put his hand upon my breast and felt my heart beat; upon which he gave me proper assistance, and at the end of three weeks I was perfectly recovered. You know, my dear Candide, I was very handsome; I became still more so, and the reverend father Croust, superior of that house, took a great fancy to me; he gave me the habit of the order, and some years afterwards I was sent to Rome. Our general stood in need of new recruits of young German Jesuits. The sovereigns of Paraguay admit as few Spanish Jesuits as possible; they prefer those of other nations, as being more obedient to command. The reverend father-general looked upon me as a proper person to work in that vineyard. I set out in company with a Polander and a Tyrolese. Upon my arrival I was honored with a subdeaconship and a lieutenancy. Now I am colonel and priest. We shall give a warm reception to the king of Spain's troops; I can assure you they will be well excommunicated and beaten. Providence has sent you hither to assist us. But is it true that my dear sister Cunégonde is in the neighborhood with the governor of Buenos Aires?"

Candide swore that nothing could be more true; and the tears began to trickle down their cheeks. The baron knew no end of embracing Candide, he called him his brother, his deliverer.

"Perhaps," said he, "my dear Candide, we shall be fortunate enough to enter the town, sword in hand, and recover my sister Cunégonde."

"Ah! that would crown my wishes," replied Candide; "for I intended to marry her; and I hope I shall still be able to do it."

"Insolent fellow!" cried the baron. "You! you have the impudence to marry my sister, who bears seventy-two quarterings! Really, I think you have an insufferable degree of assurance to dare so much as to mention such an audacious design to me."

Candide, thunderstruck at the oddness of this speech, answered: "Reverend father, all the quarterings in the world are of no meaning. I have delivered your sister from a Jew and an inquisitor; she is under many obligations to me, and she is resolved to give me her hand. My master, Pangloss, always told me that mankind are by nature equal. Therefore, you may depend upon it that I will marry your sister."

"We shall see to that, villain!" said the Jesuit baron of Thunder-ten-tronckh, and struck him across the face with the flat side of his sword. Candide in an instant drew his rapier and plunged it up to the hilt in the Jesuit's body; but in pulling it out reeking hot, he burst into tears.

"Good God!" cried he, "I have killed my old master, my friend, my brother-in-law; I am the best man in the world, and yet I have already killed three men; and of these three two were priests."

Cacambo, who was standing sentry near the door of the arbor, instantly ran up.

"Nothing remains," said his master, "but to sell our lives as dearly as possible; they will undoubtedly look into the arbor; we must die sword in hand."

Cacambo, who had seen many of this kind of adventures, was not discouraged. He stripped the baron of his Jesuit's habit and put it upon Candide, then gave him the dead man's three-cornered cap and made him mount on horseback. All this was done as quick as thought.

"Gallop, master," cried Cacambo; "everybody will take you for a Jesuit going to give orders; and we shall have passed the frontiers before they will be able to overtake us." He flew as he spoke these words, crying out loudly in Spanish, "Make way; make way for the reverend father-colonel."

Chapter XVI.

WHAT HAPPENED TO OUR TWO TRAVELLERS WITH TWO GIRLS, TWO MONKEYS, AND THE SAVAGES, CALLED OREILLONS.[1]

Candide and his valet had already passed the frontiers before it was known that the German Jesuit was dead. The wary Cacambo had taken care to fill

---

[1] From the Spanish *Orejones,* connoting "pierced ears" or "big ears." The savages wore ornaments in their ears.

his bag with bread, chocolate, some ham, some fruit, and a few bottles of wine. They penetrated with their Andalusian horses into a strange country, where they could discover no beaten path. At length a beautiful meadow, crossed with streams, opened to their view. Cacambo proposed to his master to take some nourishment, and he set him an example.

"How can you desire me to feast upon ham, when I have killed the baron's son and am doomed never more to see the beautiful Cunégonde? What will it avail me to prolong a wretched life that must be spent far from her in remorse and despair? And then what will the *Journal of Trévoux*[2] say?" was Candide's reply.

While he was making these reflections he still continued eating. The sun was now on the point of setting when the ears of our two wanderers were assailed with cries which seemed to be uttered by a female voice. They could not tell whether these were cries of grief or of joy; however, they instantly started up, full of that inquietude and apprehension which a strange place naturally inspires. The cries proceeded from two young women who were tripping disrobed along the mead, while two monkeys followed close at their heels biting at their limbs. Candide was touched with compassion; he had learned to shoot while he was among the Bulgarians, and he could hit a filbert in a hedge without touching a leaf. Accordingly he took up his double-barrelled Spanish gun, pulled the trigger, and laid the two monkeys lifeless on the ground.

"God be praised, my dear Cacambo, I have rescued two poor girls from a most perilous situation; if I have committed a sin in killing an inquisitor and a Jesuit, I have made ample amends by saving the lives of these two girls. Who knows but they may be young ladies of a good family, and that the assistance I have been so happy to give them may procure us great advantage in this country?"

He was about to continue when he felt himself struck speechless at seeing the two girls embracing the dead bodies of the monkeys in the tenderest manner, bathing their wounds with their tears, and rending the air with the most doleful lamentations.

"Really," said he to Cacambo, "I should not have expected to see such a prodigious share of good nature."

"Master," replied the knowing valet, "you have made a precious piece of work of it; do you know that you have killed the lovers of these two ladies?"

"Their lovers! Cacambo, you are jesting! It cannot be! I can never believe it."

"Dear sir," replied Cacambo, "you are surprised at everything; why

---

[2] A Jesuit journal in France founded in 1701.

should you think it so strange that there should be a country where monkeys insinuate themselves into the good graces of the ladies? They are the fourth part of a man as I am the fourth part of a Spaniard."

"Alas!" replied Candide, "I remember to have heard my master Pangloss say that such accidents as these frequently came to pass in former times, and that these mixtures produce centaurs, fauns, and satyrs; and that many of the ancients had seen such monsters; but I looked upon the whole as fabulous."

"Now you are convinced," said Cacambo, "that it is very true, and you see what use is made of those creatures by persons who have not had a proper education; all I am afraid of is that these same ladies may play us some ugly trick."

These judicious reflections operated so far on Candide as to make him quit the meadow and strike into a thicket. There he and Cacambo supped, and after heartily cursing the grand inquisitor, the governor of Buenos Aires, and the baron, they fell asleep on the ground. When they awoke they were surprised to find that they could not move; the reason was that the Oreillons who inhabit that country, and to whom the ladies had given information of these two strangers, had bound them with cords made of the bark of trees. They saw themselves surrounded by fifty naked Oreillons armed with bows and arrows, clubs, and hatchets of flint; some were making a fire under a large caldron; and others were preparing spits, crying out one and all, "A Jesuit! a Jesuit! we shall be revenged; we shall have excellent cheer; let us eat this Jesuit; let us eat him up."

"I told you, master," cried Cacambo, mournfully, "that these two wenches would play us some scurvy trick."

Candide, seeing the cauldron and the spits, cried out, "I suppose they are going either to boil or roast us. Ah! what would Pangloss say if he were to see how pure nature is formed? Everything is right; it may be so; but I must confess it is something hard to be bereft of dear Cunégonde and to be spitted like a rabbit by these barbarous Oreillons."

Cacambo, who never lost his presence of mind in distress, said to the disconsolate Candide: "Do not despair; I understand a little of the jargon of these people; I will speak to them."

"Please do," said Candide, "and be sure you remind them of the horrid barbarity of boiling and roasting human creatures, and how little of Christianity there is in such practices."

"Gentlemen," said Cacambo, "you think perhaps you are going to feast upon a Jesuit; if so, it is mighty well; nothing can be more agreeable to justice than thus to treat your enemies. Indeed the law of nature teaches us to kill our neighbor, and accordingly we find this practised all over the world; and if we do not indulge ourselves in eating human flesh, it is because we have much better fare; but for you, who have not such resources as we, it is certainly much better to feast upon your enemies than to throw their bodies to the fowls of the air, and thus lose all the fruits of your victory. But surely, gentlemen, you would not choose to eat your friends. You imagine you are going to roast a Jesuit, whereas my master is your friend, your defender, and you are going to spit the very man who has been destroying your enemies; as to myself, I am your countryman; this gentleman is my master, and so far from being a Jesuit, give me leave to tell you he has very lately killed one of that order, whose spoils he now wears, and which have probably occasioned your mistake. To convince you of the truth of what I say, take the habit he has on and carry it to the first barrier of the Jesuits' kingdom, and inquire whether my master did not kill one of their officers. There will be little or no time lost by this, and you may still reserve our bodies in your power to feast on if you should find what we have told you to be false. But, on the contrary, if you find it to be true, I am persuaded you are too well acquainted with the principles of the laws of society, humanity, and justice, not to use us courteously, and let us depart unhurt."

This speech appeared very reasonable to the Oreillons; they deputed two of their people with all diligence to inquire into the truth of this affair and acquit themselves of their commission like men of sense. The two soon returned with good tidings for our distressed adventurers. Upon this they were loosed, and those who were so lately going to roast and boil them now showed them all sorts of civilities; offered them girls, gave them refreshments, and reconducted them to the confines of their country, crying before them all the way, in token of joy: "He is no Jesuit, he is no Jesuit."

Candide could not help admiring the cause of his deliverance. "What men! what manners!" cried he; "if I had not fortunately run my sword up to the hilt in the body of Cunégonde's brother, I should have certainly been eaten alive. But, after all, pure nature is an excellent thing; since these people, instead of eating me, showed me a thousand civilities as soon as they knew I was not a Jesuit."

Chapter XVII.

CANDIDE AND HIS VALET ARRIVED IN THE COUNTRY OF EL DORADO[1] WHAT THEY SAW THERE.

When they got to the frontiers of the Oreillons, "You see," said Cacambo to Candide, "this hemisphere is not better than the other; now take my advice and let us return to Europe by the shortest way possible."

---

[1] The famous mythical country of gold that so many explorers sought in the New World.

"But how can we get back?" said Candide; "and where shall we go? To my own country? The Bulgarians and the Abares are laying that waste with fire and sword; or shall we go to Portugal? There I shall be burned; and if we abide here we are every moment in danger of being spitted. But how can I bring myself to quit that part of the world where my dear Cunégonde has her residence?"

"Let us return towards Cayenne," said Cacambo; "there we shall meet with some Frenchmen; for you know those gentry ramble all over the world; perhaps they will assist us, and God will look with pity on our distress."

It was not so easy to get to Cayenne. They knew pretty nearly whereabouts it lay; but the mountains, rivers, precipices, robbers, savages, were dreadful obstacles in the way. Their horses died with fatigue and their provisions were at an end. They subsisted a whole month on wild fruit, till at length they came to a little river bordered with cocoa trees; the sight of which at once revived their drooping spirits and furnished nourishment for their enfeebled bodies.

Cacambo, who was always giving as good advice as the old woman herself, said to Candide: "You see there is no holding out any longer; we have travelled enough on foot. I spy an empty canoe near the river side; let us fill it with cocoanuts, get into it, and go down with the stream; a river always leads to some inhabited place. If we do not meet with agreeable things, we shall at least meet with something new."

"Agreed," replied Candide; "let us recommend ourselves to Providence."

They rowed a few leagues down the river, the banks of which were in some places covered with flowers; in others barren; in some parts smooth and level, and in others steep and rugged. The stream widened as they went further on, till at length it passed under one of the frightful rocks, whose summits seemed to reach the clouds. Here our two travellers had the courage to commit themselves to the stream, which, contracting in this part, hurried them along with a dreadful noise and rapidity. At the end of twenty-four hours they saw daylight again; but their canoe was dashed to pieces against the rocks. They were obliged to creep along, from rock to rock, for the space of a league, till at length a spacious plain presented itself to their sight. This place was bounded by a chain of inaccessible mountains. The country appeared cultivated equally for pleasure and to produce the necessaries of life. The useful and agreeable were here equally blended. The roads were covered, or rather adorned, with carriages formed of glittering materials, in which were men and women of a surprising beauty, drawn with great rapidity by red sheep of a very large size; which far surpassed the finest coursers of Andalusia, Tetuan, or Mecquinez.

"Here is a country, however," said Candide, "preferable to Westphalia."

He and Cacambo landed near the first village they saw, at the entrance of which they perceived some children covered with tattered garments of the richest brocade, playing at quoits. Our two inhabitants of the other hemisphere amused themselves greatly with what they saw. The quoits were large, round pieces, yellow, red, and green, which cast a most glorious lustre. Our travellers picked some of them up, and they proved to be gold, emeralds, rubies and diamonds; the least of which would have been the greatest ornament to the superb throne of the Great Mogul.

"Without doubt," said Cacambo, "those children must be the king's sons that are playing at quoits." As he was uttering these words the schoolmaster of the village appeared, who came to call the children to school.

"There," said Candide, "is the tutor of the royal family."

The little ragamuffins immediately left their diversion, leaving the quoits on the ground with all their other playthings. Candide gathered them up, ran to the schoolmaster, and, with a most respectful bow, presented them to him, giving him to understand by signs that their royal highnesses had forgot their gold and precious stones. The schoolmaster, with a smile, flung them upon the ground, then examining Candide from head to foot with an air of admiration, he turned his back and went on his way.

Our travellers took care, however, to gather up the gold, the rubies, and the emeralds.

"Where are we?" cried Candide. "The king's children in this country must have an excellent education, since they are taught to show such a contempt for gold and precious stones."

Cacambo was as much surprised as his master. They then drew near the first house in the village, which was built after the manner of a European palace. There was a crowd of people about the door, and a still greater number in the house. The sound of the most delightful instruments of music was heard, and the most agreeable smell came from the kitchen. Cacambo went up to the door and heard those within talking in the Peruvian language, which was his mother tongue; for every one knows that Cacambo was born in a village of Tucuman, where no other language is spoken.

"I will be your interpreter here," said he to Candide. "Let us go in; this is an inn."

Immediately two waiters and two servant-girls, dressed in cloth of gold, and their hair braided with ribbons of tissue, accosted the strangers and invited them to sit down to the table. Their dinner consisted of four dishes of different soups, each garnished with two young paroquets, a large dish of bouillé that weighed two hundred pounds, two roasted monkeys of a delicious flavor, three hundred humming-birds in one dish, and six hundred fly-birds in another; some excellent ragouts, delicate tarts, and the whole served up in dishes of rock-crystal. Several sorts of liquors, extracted from the sugar-cane, were handed about by the servants who attended.

Most of the company were tradesmen and coachmen, all extremely polite; they asked Cacambo a few questions with the utmost discretion and circumspection; and replied to his in a most obliging and satisfactory manner.

As soon as dinner was over, both Candide and Cacambo thought they should pay very handsomely for their entertainment by laying down two of those large gold pieces which they had picked off the ground; but the landlord and landlady burst into a fit of laughing and held their sides for some time. When the fit was over, "Gentlemen," said the landlord, "I plainly perceive you are strangers, and such we are not accustomed to charge; pardon us, therefore, for laughing when you offered us the common pebbles of our highways for payment of your reckoning. To be sure, you have none of the coin of this kingdom; but there is no necessity of having any money at all to dine in this house. All the inns, which are established for the convenience of those who carry on the trade of this nation, are maintained by the government. You have found but very indifferent entertainment here, because this is only a poor village; but in almost every other of these public houses you will meet with a reception worthy of persons of your merit." Cacambo explained the whole of this speech of the landlord to Candide, who listened to it with the same astonishment with which his friend communicated it.

"What sort of a country is this," said the one to the other, "that is unknown to all the world; and in which Nature has everywhere so different an appearance to what she has in ours? Possibly this is the part of the globe where everything is right, for there must certainly be some such place. And, for all that Master Pangloss could say, I often perceived that things went very ill in Westphalia."

Chapter XVIII.

WHAT THEY SAW IN THE COUNTRY OF EL DORADO.

Cacambo vented all his curiosity upon his landlord by a thousand different questions; the honest man answered him thus: "I am very ignorant, sir, but I am contented with my ignorance; however, we have in this neighborhood an old man retired from court, who is the most learned and communicative person in the whole kingdom." He then conducted Cacambo to the old man; Candide acted now only a second character, and attended his valet. They entered a very plain house, for the door was nothing but silver, and the ceiling was only of beaten gold, but wrought in such elegant taste as to vie with the richest. The antechamber, indeed, was only incrusted with rubies and emeralds; but the order in which everything was disposed made amends for this great simplicity.

The old man received the strangers on his sofa, which was stuffed with humming-birds' feathers; and ordered his servants to present them with liquors in golden goblets, after which he satisfied their curiosity in the following terms:

"I am now one hundred and seventy-two years old, and I learned of my late father, who was equerry to the king, the amazing revolutions of Peru, to which he had been an eye-witness. This kingdom is the ancient patrimony of the Incas, who very imprudently quitted it to conquer another part of the world, and were at length conquered and destroyed themselves by the Spaniards.

"Those princes of their family who remained in their native country acted more wisely. They ordained, with the consent of their whole nation, that none of the inhabitants of our little kingdom should ever quit it; and to this wise ordinance we owe the preservation of our innocence and happiness. The Spaniards had some confused notion of this country, to which they gave the name of *El Dorado;* and Sir Walter Raleigh, an Englishman, actually came very near it about three hundred years ago; but the inaccessible rocks and precipices with which our country is surrounded on all sides, has hitherto secured us from the rapacious fury of the people of Europe, who have an unaccountable fondness for the pebbles and dirt of our land, for the sake of which they would murder us all to the very last man."

The conversation lasted some time and turned chiefly on the form of government, their manners, their women, their public diversions, and the arts. At length, Candide, who had always had a taste for metaphysics, asked whether the people of that country had any religion.

The old man reddened a little at this question.

"Can you doubt it?" said he; "do you take us for wretches lost to all sense of gratitude?"

Cacambo asked in a respectful manner what was the established religion of El Dorado. The old man blushed again, and said: "Can there be two religions, then? Ours, I apprehend, is the religion of the whole world; we worship God from morning till night."

"Do you worship but one God?" said Cacambo, who still acted as the interpreter of Candide's doubts.

"Certainly," said the old man; "there are not two, nor three, nor four Gods. I must confess the people of your world ask very extraordinary questions."

However, Candide could not refrain from making many more inquiries of the old man; he wanted to know in what manner they prayed to God in El Dorado.

"We do not pray to him at all," said the reverend sage; "we have nothing to ask of Him. He has given us all we want, and we give Him thanks incessantly." Candide had a curiosity to see some of their priests, and desired Cacambo to ask the old man where they were. At which he smiling said:

"My friends, we are all of us priests; the king and all the heads of families sing solemn hymns of thanksgiving every morning, accompanied by five or six thousand musicians."

"What!" said Cacambo, "have you no monks among you to dispute, to govern, to intrigue, and to burn people who are not of the same opinion with themselves?"

"Do you take us for fools?" said the old man. "Here we are all of one opinion, and know not what you mean by your monks."

During the whole of this discourse Candide was in raptures, and he said to himself, "What a prodigious difference is there between this place and Westphalia; and this house and the baron's castle. Ah, Master Pangloss! had you ever seen El Dorado, you would no longer have maintained that the castle of Thunder-ten-tronckh was the finest of all possible edifices; there is nothing like seeing the world, that's certain."

This long conversation being ended, the old man ordered six sheep to be harnessed and put to the coach, and sent twelve of his servants to escort the travellers to court.

"Excuse me," said he, "for not waiting on you in person, my age deprives me of that honor. The king will receive you in such a manner that you will have no reason to complain; and doubtless you will make a proper allowance for the customs of the country if they should not happen altogther to please you."

Candide and Cacambo got into the coach, the six sheep flew, and, in less than a quarter of an hour, they arrived at the king's palace, which was situated at the further end of the capital. At the entrance was a portal two hundred and twenty feet high and one hundred wide; but it is impossible for words to express the materials of which it was built. The reader, however, will readily conceive that they must have a prodigious superiority over the pebbles and sand, which we call gold and precious stones.

Twenty beautiful young virgins in waiting received Candide and Cacambo on their alighting from the coach, conducted them to the bath and clad them in robes woven of the down of humming-birds; after which they were introduced by the great officers of the crown of both sexes to the king's apartment, between two files of musicians, each file consisting of a thousand, agreeable to the custom of the country. When they drew near to the presence-chamber, Cacambo asked one of the officers in what manner they were to pay their obeisance to his majesty; whether it was the custom to fall upon their knees, or to prostrate themselves upon the ground; whether they were to put their hands upon their heads, or behind their backs; whether they were to lick the dust off the floor; in short, what was the ceremony usual on such occasions.

"The custom," said the great officer, "is to embrace the king and kiss him on each cheek."

Candide and Cacambo accordingly threw their arms round his majesty's neck, who received them in the most gracious manner imaginable, and very politely asked them to sup with him.

While supper was preparing orders were given to show them the city, where they saw public structures that reared their lofty heads to the clouds; the market-places decorated with a thousand columns; fountains of spring water, besides others of rose water, and of liquors drawn from the sugar-cane, incessantly flowing in the great squares; which were paved with a kind of precious stones that emitted an odor like that of cloves and cinnamon. Candide asked to see the high court of justice, the parliament; but was answered that they had none in that country, being utter strangers to lawsuits. He then inquired if they had any prisons; they replied none. But what gave him at once the greatest surprise and pleasure was the palace of sciences, where he saw a gallery two thousand feet long, filled with the various apparatus in mathematics and natural philosophy.

After having spent the whole afternoon in seeing only about the thousandth part of the city, they were brought back to the king's palace. Candide sat down at the table with his majesty, his valet Cacambo, and several ladies of the court. Never was entertainment more elegant, nor could any one possibly show more wit than his majesty displayed while they were at supper. Cacambo explained all the king's *bons mots* to Candide, and, although they were translated, they still appeared to be *bons mots*. Of all the things that surprised Candide, this was not the least. They spent a whole month in this hospitable place, during which time Candide was continually saying to Cacambo:

"I own, my friend, once more, that the castle where I was born is a mere nothing in comparison to the place where we now are; but still Cunégonde is not here, and you yourself have doubtless some fair one in Europe for whom you sigh. If we remain here we shall only be as others are; whereas, if we return to our own world with only a dozen of El Dorado sheep, loaded with the pebbles of this country, we shall be richer than all the kings in Europe; we shall no longer need to stand in awe of the inquisitors; and we may easily recover Cunégonde."

This speech was perfectly agreeable to Cacambo. A fondness for roving, for making a figure in their own country, and for boasting of what they had seen in their travels, was so powerful in our two wanderers that they resolved to be no longer happy; and demanded permission of the king to quit the country.

"You are about to do a rash and silly action," said the king. "I am sensible my kingdom is an inconsiderable spot; but when people are tolerably at their ease in any place, I should think it would be to their interest to remain there. Most assuredly, I have no right to detain you, or any strangers, against your wills; this is an act of tyranny to which our manners and our laws are equally repugnant; all men are by nature free; you have therefore an undoubted liberty to depart whenever you please, but you will have many and great difficulties to encounter in passing the frontiers. It is impossible to ascend that rapid river which runs under high and vaulted rocks, and by which you were conveyed hither by a kind of miracle. The mountains by which my kingdom are hemmed in on all sides, are ten thousand feet high, and perfectly perpendicular; they are above ten leagues across, and the descent from them is one continued precipice. However, since you are determined to leave us, I will immediately give orders to the superintendent of my carriages to cause one to be made that will convey you very safely. When they have conducted you to the back of the mountains, nobody can attend you farther; for my subjects have made a vow never to quit the kingdom, and they are too prudent to break it. Ask me whatever else you please."

"All we shall ask of your majesty," said Cacambo, "is only a few sheep laden with provisions, pebbles, and the clay of your country."

The king smiled at the request, and said: "I cannot imagine what pleasure you Europeans find in our yellow clay; but take away as much of it as you will, and much good may it do you."

He immediately gave orders to his engineers to make a machine to hoist these two extraordinary men out of the kingdom. Three thousand good machinists went to work and finished it in about fifteen days, and it did not cost more than twenty millions sterling of that country's money. Candide and Cacambo were placed on this machine, and they took with them two large red sheep, bridled and saddled, to ride upon, when they got on the other side of the mountains; twenty others to serve as sumpters for carrying provisions; thirty laden with presents of whatever was most curious in the country, and fifty with gold, diamonds, and other precious stones. The king, at parting with our two adventurers, embraced them with the greatest cordiality.

It was a curious sight to behold the manner of their setting off, and the ingenious method by which they and their sheep were hoisted to the top of the mountains. The machinists and engineers took leave of them as soon as they had conveyed them to a place of safety, and Candide was wholly occupied with the thoughts of presenting his sheep to Cunégonde.

"Now," cried he, "thanks to heaven, we have more than sufficient to pay the governor of Buenos Aires for Cunégonde, if she is redeemable. Let us make the best of our way to Cayenne, where we will take shipping and then we may at leisure think of what kingdom we shall purchase with our riches.

Chapter XIX.

WHAT HAPPENED TO THEM AT SURINAM, AND HOW CANDIDE BECAME ACQUAINTED WITH MARTIN.

Our travellers' first day's journey was very pleasant; they were elated with the prospect of possessing more riches than were to be found in Europe, Asia, and Africa together. Candide, in an ecstasy, cut the name of Cunégonde on almost every tree he came to. The second day two of their sheep sunk in a morass, and were swallowed up with their loads; two more died of fatigue; some few days afterwards seven or eight perished with hunger in a desert, and others, at different times, tumbled down precipices, or were otherwise lost, so that, after travelling about a hundred days they had only two sheep left of the hundred and two they brought with them from El Dorado. Said Candide to Cacambo:

"You see, my dear friend, how perishable the riches of this world are; there is nothing solid but virtue."

"Very true," said Cacambo, "but we have still two sheep remaining, with more treasure than ever the king of Spain will be possessed of; and I see a town at a distance, which I take to be Surinam, a town belonging to the Dutch. We are now at the end of our troubles, and at the beginning of happiness."

As they drew near the town they saw a Negro stretched on the ground with only one half of his habit, which was a kind of linen frock; for the poor man had lost his left leg and his right hand.

"Good God," said Candide in Dutch, "what dost thou here, friend, in this deplorable condition?"

"I am waiting for my master, Mynheer Vanderdendur, the famous trader," answered the Negro.

"Was it Mynheer Vanderdendur that used you in this cruel manner?"

"Yes, sir," said the Negro; "it is the custom here. They give us a linen garment twice a year, and that is all our covering. When we labor in the sugar works, and the mill happens to snatch hold of a finger, they instantly chop off our hand; and when we attempt to run away, they cut off a leg. Both these cases have happened to me, and it is at this expense that you eat sugar in Europe; and yet when my mother sold me for ten patacoons on the coast of Guinea, she said to me, 'My dear child, bless our fetishes; adore them forever; they will make you live happy; you have the honor to be a slave to our lords the whites, by which you will make the fortune of us your parents.' Alas! I don't know whether I have made their fortunes; but they have not made mine: dogs, monkeys, and parrots are a thousand times less wretched than I. The Dutch fetishes who converted me tell me every Sunday that the blacks and whites are all children of one father, whom they call Adam. As for me, I do not understand anything of genealogies; but if what these preachers say is true, we are all second cousins; and you must allow that it is impossible to be worse treated by our relations than we are."

"O Pangloss!" cried Candide, "such horrid doings never entered your imagination. Here is an end of the matter; I find myself, after all, obliged to renounce your Optimism."

"Optimism," said Cacambo, "what is that?"

"Alas!" replied Candide, "it is the obstinacy of maintaining that everything is best when it is worst." And so saying he turned his eyes towards the poor Negro, and shed a flood of tears; and in this weeping mood he entered the town of Surinam.

Immediately upon their arrival our travellers inquired if there was any vessel in the harbor which they might sent to Buenos Aires. The person they addressed themselves to happened to be the master of a Spanish ship, who offered to agree with them on moderate terms, and appointed them a meeting at an inn. Candide and his faithful Cacambo went there to wait for him, taking with them their two sheep.

Candide, who was all frankness and sincerity, made an ingenuous recital of his adventures to the Spaniard, declaring to him at the same time his resolution of carrying off Cunégonde from the governor of Buenos Aires.

"O ho!" said the shipmaster, "if that is the case, get whom you please to carry you to Buenos Aires; for my part, I wash my hands of the affair. It would prove a hanging matter to us all. The fair Cunégonde is the governor's favorite mistress." These words were like a clap of thunder to Candide; he wept bitterly for a long time, and, taking Cacambo aside, he said to him, "I'll tell you, my dear friend, what you must do. We have each of us in our pockets to the value of five or six millions in diamonds; you are cleverer at these matters than I; you must go to Buenos Aires and bring off Miss Cunégonde. If the governor makes any difficulty give him a million; if he holds out, give him two; as you have not killed an inquisitor, they will have no suspicion of you. I'll fit out another ship and go to Venice, where I will wait for you. Venice is a free country, where we shall have nothing to fear from Bulgarians, Abarians, Jews, or Inquisitors."

Cacambo greatly applauded this wise resolution. He was inconsolable at the thoughts of parting with so good a master, who treated him more like an intimate friend than a servant; but the pleasure of being able to do him a service soon got the better of his sorrow. They embraced each other with a flood of tears. Candide charged him not to forget the old woman. Cacambo set out the same day. This Cacambo was a very honest fellow.

Candide continued some days longer at Surinam, waiting for any captain to carry him and his two remaining sheep to Italy. He hired domestics, and purchased many things necessary for a long voyage; at length Mynheer Vanderdendur, skipper of a large Dutch vessel, came and offered his service.

"What will you have," said Candide, "to carry me, my servants, my baggage, and these two sheep you see here, directly to Venice?"

The skipper asked ten thousand piastres, and Candide agreed to his demand without hesitation.

"Oho!" said the cunning Vanderdendur to himself, "this stranger must be very rich; he agrees to give me ten thousand piastres without hesitation." Returning a little while after he tells Candide that upon second consideration he could not undertake the voyage for less than twenty thousand.

"Very well; you shall have them," said Candide.

"Zounds!" said the skipper to himself, "this man agrees to pay twenty thousand piastres with as much ease as ten." Accordingly he goes back again, and tells him roundly that he will not carry him to Venice for less than thirty thousand piastres.

"Then you shall have thirty thousand," said Candide.

"Oh!" said the Dutchman once more to himself, "thirty thousand piastres seem a trifle to this man. Those sheep must certainly be laden with an immense treasure. I'll even stop here and ask no more; but make him pay down the thirty thousand piastres, and then we may see what is to be done farther." Candide sold two small diamonds, the least of which was worth more than all the skipper asked. He paid him beforehand, the two sheep were put on board, and Candide followed in a small boat to join the vessel in the road. The skipper took advantage of his opportunity, hoisted sail, and put out to sea with a favorable wind. Candide, confounded and amazed, soon lost sight of the ship. "Alas!" said he, "this is a trick like those in our old world!"

He returned back to the shore overwhelmed with grief; and, indeed, he had lost what would have made the fortune of twenty monarchs.

Straightway upon his landing he applied to the Dutch magistrate; being somewhat nervous, he thundered at the door. He went in, told his case, and talked a little louder than was necessary. The magistrate began with fining him ten thousand piastres for his petulance, and then listened very patiently to what he had to say, promised to examine into the affair on the skipper's return, and ordered him to pay ten thousand piastres more for the fees of the court.

This treatment put Candide out of all patience; it is true, he had suffered misfortunes a thousand times more grievous, but the cool insolence of the judge, and the villainy of the skipper raised his ill humor and threw him into a deep melancholy. The villainy of mankind presented itself to his mind in all its deformity, and he was a prey to the most gloomy ideas. After some time, hearing that a French ship was ready to set sail for Bordeaux, since there were no more sheep loaded with diamonds to put on board, he hired the cabin at the usual price; and made it known in the town that he would pay the passage and board of any honest man who would give him his company during the voyage; besides making him a present of ten thousand piastres, on condition that such person was the most dissatisfied with his condition, and the most unfortunate in the whole province.

At this there appeared such a crowd of candidates that a large fleet could not have contained them. Candide, willing to choose from among those who appeared most likely to answer his intention, selected twenty, who seemed to him the most sociable, and who all pretended to merit the preference. He invited them to his inn, and promised to treat them with a supper, on condition that every man should bind himself by an oath to relate his own history; declaring at the same time, that he would choose that person who should appear to him the most deserving of compassion, and the most justly dissatisfied with his condition in life; and that he would make a present to the rest.

This extraordinary assembly continued sitting till four in the morning. Candide, while he was listening to their adventures, called to mind what the old woman had said to him in their voyage to Buenos Aires, and the wager she had laid that there was scarcely a person on board the ship who had not met with great misfortunes. Every story he heard put him in mind of Pangloss.

"My old master," said he, "would be confoundedly put to it to demonstrate his favorite system. Would he were here! Certainly if everything is for the best, it is in El Dorado; and not in the other parts of the world."

At length he determined in favor of a poor scholar, who had labored ten years for the booksellers at Amsterdam.[1] He thought that no employment could be more detestable.

This scholar, who was in fact a very honest man, had been robbed by his wife, beaten by his son, and forsaken by his daughter, who had run away with a Portuguese. He had been likewise deprived of a small employment on which he subsisted, and he was persecuted by the clergy of Surinam, who took him for a Socinian.[2] It must be acknowledged that the other competi-

---

[1] Voltaire suffered from the pirating of his works in Holland where there was freedom of the press and no international copyright laws.

[2] The Socinians denied among other things the Trinity, original sin, and the divinity of Christ.

tors were, at least, as wretched as he; but Candide was in hopes that the company of a man of letters would relieve the tediousness of the voyage. All the other candidates complained that Candide had done them a great injustice, but he silenced them by a present of a hundred piastres to each.

Chapter XX.

WHAT BEFELL CANDIDE AND MARTIN ON THEIR PASSAGE.

The old philosopher, whose name was Martin, embarked with Candide for Bordeaux. Both had seen and suffered a great deal, and had the ship been going from Surinam to Japan round the Cape of Good Hope, they could have found sufficient entertainment for each other during the whole voyage, in discoursing upon moral and natural evil.

Candide, however, had one advantage over Martin: he lived in the pleasing hopes of seeing Cunégonde once more; whereas, the poor philosopher had nothing to hope for; besides, Candide had money and jewels, and, notwithstanding he had lost a hundred red sheep laden with the greatest treasure outside of El Dorado, and though he still smarted from the reflection of the Dutch skipper's knavery, yet when he considered what he had still left, and repeated the name of Cunégonde, especially after meal times, he inclined to Pangloss' doctrine.

"And pray," said he to Martin, "what is your opinion of the whole of this system? what notion have you of moral and natural evil?"

"Sir," replied Martin, "our priest accused me of being a Socinian; but the real truth is, I am a Manichaean."[1]

"Nay, now you are jesting," said Candide; "there are no Manichaeans existing at present in the world."

"And yet I am one," said Martin; "but I cannot help it. I cannot for the soul of me think otherwise."

"Surely the devil must be in you," said Candide.

"He concerns himself so much," replied Martin, "in the affairs of this world that it is very probable he may be in me as well as everywhere else; but I must confess, when I cast my eye on this globe, or rather globule, I cannot help thinking that God has abandoned it to some malignant being. I always except El Dorado. I scarce ever knew a city that did not wish the destruction of its neighboring city; nor a family that did not desire to

---

[1] A follower of the doctrine of the Persian Manichaeus who believed that good and evil are of approximately equal strength, one not able to overcome the other.

exterminate some other family. The poor in all parts of the world bear an inveterate hatred to the rich, even while they creep and cringe to them; and the rich treat the poor like sheep, whose wool and flesh they barter for money; a million of regimented assassins cross Europe from one end to the other, to get their bread by regular robbery and murder, because it is the most gentlemanlike profession. Even in those cities which seem to enjoy the blessings of peace, and where the arts flourish, the inhabitants are devoured with envy, care, and inquietudes, which are greater plagues than any experienced in a town besieged. Private chagrins are still more dreadful than public calamities. In a word," concluded the philosopher, "I have seen and suffered so much that I am a Manichaean."

"And yet there is some good in the world," replied Candide.

"May be so," said Martin, "but it has escaped my knowledge."

While they were deeply engaged in this dispute they heard the report of cannon, which redoubled every moment. Each took out his glass, and they spied two ships warmly engaged at the distance of about three miles. The wind brought them both so near the French ship that those on board her had the pleasure of seeing the fight with great ease. After several smart broadsides the one gave the other a shot between wind and water which sunk her outright. Then could Candide and Martin plainly perceive a hundred men on the deck of the vessel which was sinking, who, with hands uplifted to heaven, sent forth piercing cries, and were in a moment swallowed up by the waves.

"Well," said Martin, "you now see in what manner men treat one another."

"It is certain," said Candide, "that there is something diabolical in this affair." As he was speaking thus he spied something of a shining red hue, which swam close to the vessel. The boat was hoisted out to see what it might be, when it proved to be one of his sheep. Candide felt more joy at the recovery of this one animal than he did grief when he lost the other hundred, though laden with the large diamonds of El Dorado.

The French captain quickly perceived that the victorious ship belonged to the crown of Spain; that the other was a Dutch pirate, and the very same captain who had robbed Candide. The immense riches which this villain had amassed, were buried with him in the deep, and this one sheep saved out of the whole.

"You see," said Candide to Martin, "that vice is sometimes punished; this villain, the Dutch skipper, has met with the fate he deserved."

"Very true," said Martin, "but why should the passengers be doomed also to destruction? God has punished the knave, and the devil has drowned the rest."

The French and Spanish ships continued their cruise, and Candide and

Martin their conversation. They disputed fourteen days successively, at the end of which they were just as far advanced as the first moment they began. However, they had the satisfaction of disputing, of communicating their ideas, and of mutually comforting each other. Candide embraced his sheep with ecstasy.

"Since I have found thee again," said he, "I may possibly find my Cunégonde once more."

Chapter XXI.

CANDIDE AND MARTIN, WHILE THUS REASONING WITH EACH OTHER, DRAW NEAR TO THE COAST OF FRANCE.

At length they sighted the coast of France, when Candide said to Martin, "Were you ever in France?"

"Yes sir," said Martin, "I have been in several provinces of that kingdom. In some, one-half of the people are fools and madmen; in some, they are too artful; in others, again, they are, in general, either very good-natured or very brutal; while in others, they affect to be witty, and in all, their ruling passion is love, the next is slander, and the last is to talk nonsense."

"But were you ever in Paris?"

"Yes, sir, I have been in that city, and it is a place that contains the several species just described; it is a chaos, a confused multitude, where everyone seeks for pleasure without being able to find it; at least, as far as I have observed during my short stay in that city. At my arrival I was robbed of all I had in the world by pickpockets and sharpers, at the fair of St. Germain. I was taken up myself for a robber, and confined in prison a whole week; after which I hired myself as corrector to a press, in order to get a little money towards defraying my expenses back to Holland on foot. I knew the whole tribe of scribblers, malcontents, and fanatics. It is said the people of that city are very polite; I believe they may be."

"For my part, I have no curiosity to see France," said Candide; "you may easily conceive, my friend, that after spending a month in El Dorado, I can desire to behold nothing upon earth but Cunégonde; I am going to wait for her at Venice. I intend to pass through France, on my way to Italy. Will you not bear me company?" "With all my heart," said Martin; "they say Venice is agreeable to none but noble Venetians; but that, nevertheless, strangers are well received there when they have plenty of money; now I have none, but you have, therefore I will attend you wherever you please."

"Now we are upon this subject," said Candide, "do you think that the earth was originally sea, as we read in that great book[1] which belongs to the captain of the ship?" "I believe nothing of it," replied Martin, "any more than I do of the many other chimeras which have been related to us for some time past." "But then, to what end," said Candide, "was the world formed?" "To make us mad," said Martin. "Are you not surprised," continued Candide "at the love which the two girls in the country of the Oreillons had for those two monkeys?—You know I have told you the story." "Surprised?" replied Martin, "not in the least; I see nothing strange in this passion. I have seen so many extraordinary things that there is nothing extraordinary to me now." "Do you think," said Candide, "that men always massacred one another as they do now? were they always guilty of lies, fraud, treachery, ingratitude, inconstancy, envy, ambition, and cruelty? were they always thieves, fools, cowards, gluttons, drunkards, misers, calumniators, debauchees, fanatics, and hypocrites?" "Do you believe," said Martin, "that hawks have always been accustomed to eat pigeons when they came in their way?" "Doubtless," said Candide. "Well then," replied Martin, "if hawks have always had the same nature, why should you pretend that mankind change theirs?" "Oh," said Candide, "there is a great deal of difference; for free will—" and reasoning thus they arrived at Bordeaux.

[In Chapter 22, Candide and Martin go to Paris. Candide grows sick and eventually is cured. He loses a large sum of money at gambling and even has two of his diamond rings stolen. A priest, who hears about Cunégonde, hires a woman to impersonate her and Candide unwittingly gives her most of his diamonds. The police arrest Candide and Martin as suspicious foreigners, but they are bribed. Candide and Martin sail for England.]

Chapter XXIII.

CANDIDE AND MARTIN TOUCH UPON THE ENGLISH
COAST—WHAT THEY SEE THERE.

"Ah Pangloss! Pangloss! ah Martin! Martin! ah my dear Cunégonde! what sort of a world is this?" Thus exclaimed Candide as soon as he got

---

[1] The Bible or possibly Buffon's *Theorie de la terre* (1749).

on board the Dutch ship. "Why something very foolish, and very abominable," said Martin. "You are acquainted with England," said Candide; "are they as great fools in that country as in France?" "Yes, but in a different manner," answered Martin. "You know that these two nations are at war about a few acres of barren land in the neighborhood of Canada,[1] and that they have expended much greater sums in the contest than all Canada is worth. To say exactly whether there are a greater number fit to be inhabitants of a madhouse in the one country than the other, exceeds the limits of my imperfect capacity; I know in general that the people we are going to visit are of a very dark and gloomy disposition."

As they were chatting thus together they arrived at Portsmouth. The shore on each side the harbor was lined with a multitude of people, whose eyes were steadfastly fixed on a large man who was kneeling down on the deck of one of the men-of-war, with something tied before his eyes. Opposite to this personage stood four soldiers, each of whom shot three bullets into his skull, with all the composure imaginable; and when it was done, the whole company went away perfectly well satisfied. "What the devil is all this for?" said Candide, "and what demon, or foe of mankind, lords it thus tyrannically over the world?" He then asked who was that large man who had been sent out of the world with so much ceremony. When he received for answer, that it was an admiral. "And why do you put your admiral to death?"[2] "Because he did not put a sufficient number of his fellow-creatures to death. You must know, he had an engagement with a French admiral, and it has been proved against him that he was not near enough to his antagonist." "But," replied Candide, "the French admiral must have been as far from him." "There is no doubt of that; but in this country it is found requisite, now and then, to put an admiral to death, in order to encourage the others to fight."

Candide was so shocked at what he saw and heard, that he would not set foot on shore, but made a bargain with the Dutch skipper (were he even to rob him like the captain of Surinam) to carry him directly to Venice.

The skipper was ready in two days. They sailed along the coast of France, and passed within sight of Lisbon, at which Candide trembled. From thence they proceeded to the Straits, entered the Mediterranean, and at length arrived at Venice. "God be praised," said Candide, embracing Martin, "this is the place where I am to behold my beloved Cunégonde once again. I can confide in Cacambo, like another self. All is well, all very well, all as well as possible."

---

1 French and Indian War (1754-1763).

2 Admiral Byng was executed on March 14, 1757, for failing to win a naval engagement against the French the previous year. Voltaire had attempted to save his life.

[In Chapter 24, Candide and Martin travel to Venice. They do not find Cacambo, but they see Paquette, Pangloss' former mistress, who helps them. Candide goes to visit the nobleman Pococuranté, who has never known grief.]

Chapter XXV.

CANDIDE AND MARTIN PAY A VISIT TO LORD POCO-CURANTÉ, A NOBLE VENETIAN.

Candide and his friend Martin went in a gondola on the Brenta, and arrived at the palace of the noble Pococuranté. The gardens were laid out in elegant taste, and adorned with fine marble statues; his palace was built after the most approved rules of architecture. The master of the house, who was a man of affairs, and very rich, received our two travellers with great politeness, but without much ceremony, which somewhat disconcerted Candide, but was not at all displeasing to Martin.

As soon as they were seated, two very pretty girls, neatly dressed, brought in chocolate, which was extremely well prepared. Candide could not help praising their beauty and graceful carriage. "The creatures are well enough," said the senator; "I amuse myself with them sometimes, for I am heartily tired of the women of the town, their coquetry, their jealousy, their quarrels, their humors, their meannesses, their pride, and their folly; I am weary of making sonnets, or of paying for sonnets to be made on them; but after all, these two girls begin to grow very indifferent to me."

After having refreshed himself, Candide walked into a large gallery, where he was struck with the sight of a fine collection of paintings. Candide asked what master painted the two first of these." "They are by Raphael," answered the senator. "I gave a great deal of money for them seven years ago, purely out of curiosity, as they were said to be the finest pieces in Italy; but I cannot say they please me: the coloring is dark and heavy; the figures do not swell nor come out enough; and the drapery is bad. In short, notwithstanding the praise lavished upon them, they are not, in my opinion, a true representation of nature. I approve of no paintings save those wherein I think I behold nature herself; and there are few, if any, of that kind to be met with. I have what is called a fine collection, but I take no manner of delight in it."

While dinner was being prepared Pococuranté ordered a concert. Candide praised the music to the skies. "This noise," said the noble Venetian, "may amuse one for a little time, but if it were to last above half an hour, it would grow tiresome to everybody, though perhaps no one would care to own it. Music has become the art of executing what is difficult; now, whatever is difficult cannot be long pleasing.

"I believe I might take more pleasure in an opera, if they had not made such a monster of that species of dramatic entertainment as perfectly shocks me; and I am amazed how people can bear to see wretched tragedies set to music; where the scenes are contrived for no other purpose than to lug in, as it were by the ears, three or four ridiculous songs, to give a favorite actress an opportunity of exhibiting her pipe. Let who will die away in raptures at the trills of a eunuch quavering the majestic part of Cæsar or Cato, and strutting in a foolish manner upon the stage, but for my part I have long ago renounced these paltry entertainments, which constitute the glory of modern Italy, and are so dearly purchased by crowned heads." Candide opposed these sentiments; but he did it in a discreet manner; as for Martin, he was entirely of the old senator's opinion.

Dinner being served, they sat down to table, and, after a hearty repast, returned to the library. Candide, observing Homer richly bound, commended the noble Venetian's taste. "This," said he, "is a book that was once the delight of the great Pangloss, the best philosopher in Germany." "Homer is no favorite of mine," answered Pococuranté, cooly; "I was made to believe once that I took a pleasure in reading him; but his continual repetition of battles have all such a resemblance with each other; his gods that are forever in haste and bustle, without ever doing anything; his Helen, who is the cause of the war, and yet hardly acts in the whole performance; his Troy, that holds out so long, without being taken: in short, all these things together make the poem very insipid to me. I have asked some learned men, whether they are not in reality as much tired as myself with reading this poet: those who spoke ingenuously, assured me that he had made them fall asleep, and yet that they could not well avoid giving him a place in their libraries; but that it was merely as they would do an antique, or those rusty medals which are kept only for curiosity, and are of no manner of use in commerce."

"But your excellency does not surely form the same opinion of Virgil?" said Candide. "Why, I grant," replied Pococuranté, "that the second, third, fourth, and sixth books of his "Æneid" are excellent; but as for his pious Æneas, his strong Cloanthes, his friendly Achates, his boy Ascanius, his silly King Latinus, his ill-bred Amata, his insipid Lavinia, and some other characters much in the same strain, I think there cannot in nature be anything more flat and disagreeable. I must confess I prefer Tasso far beyond him; nay, even that sleepy tale-teller Ariosto."[1]

---

[1] Tasso (1544-1595) and Ariosto (1474-1533), Italian poets, were two of Voltaire's favorite authors.

"May I take the liberty to ask if you do not experience great pleasure from reading Horace?" said Candide. "There are maxims in this writer," replied Pococuranté, "whence a man of the world may reap some benefit; and the short measure of the verse makes them more easily to be retained in the memory. But I see nothing extraordinary in his journey to Brundusium, and his account of his bad dinner; nor in his dirty, low quarrel between one Rupilius,[2] whose words, as he expresses it, were full of poisonous filth; and another, whose language was dipped in vinegar. His indelicate verses against old women and witches have frequently given me great offence: nor can I discover the great merit of his telling his friend Mæcenas, that if he will but rank him in the class of lyric poets, his lofty head shall touch the stars. Ignorant readers are apt to judge a writer by his reputation. For my part, I read only to please myself. I like nothing but what makes for my purpose." Candide, who had been brought up with a notion of never making use of his own judgment, was astonished at what he heard; but Martin found there was a good deal of reason in the senator's remarks.

"O! here is a Cicero," said Candide; "this great man I fancy you are never tired of reading?" "Indeed I never read him at all," replied Pococuranté. "What is it to me whether he pleads for Rabirius or Cluentius? I try causes enough myself. I had once some liking for his philosophical works; but when I found he doubted everything, I thought I knew as much as himself, and had no need of a guide to learn ignorance."

"Ha!" cried Martin, "here are eighty volumes of the proceedings of the Academy of Sciences; perhaps there may be something curious and valuable in this collection." "Yes," answered Pococuranté; "so there might if any one of these compilers of this rubbish had only invented the art of pinmaking: but all these volumes are filled with empty systems, without one single article conducive to real utility."

"I see a prodigious number of plays," said Candide, "in Italian, Spanish, and French." "Yes," replied the Venetian; "there are I think three thousand, and not three dozen of them good for anything. As to those huge volumes of divinity, and those enormous collections of sermons, they are not all together worth one single page in Seneca; and I fancy you will readily believe that neither myself, nor anyone else, ever looks into them."

Martin, perceiving some shelves filled with English books, said to the senator: "I fancy that a republican must be highly delighted with those books, which are most of them written with a noble spirit of freedom." "It is noble to write as we think," said Pococuranté; "it is the privilege of humanity. Throughout Italy we write only what we do not think; and the present inhabitants of the country of the Cæsars and Antonines dare not

---

[2] "Rupilius" in Horace's *Satires*, I, vii.

acquire a single idea without the permission of a Dominican father.[3] I should be enamored of the spirit of the English nation, did it not utterly frustrate the good effects it would produce by passion and the spirit of party."

Candide, seeing a Milton, asked the senator if he did not think that author a great man. "Who?" said Pococuranté sharply; "that barbarian who writes a tedious commentary in ten books of rumbling verse, on the first chapter of Genesis?[4] That slovenly imitator of the Greeks, who disfigures the creation, by making the Messiah take a pair of compasses from heaven's armory to plan the world; whereas Moses represented the Deity as producing the whole universe by his *fiat?* Can I think you have any esteem for a writer who has spoiled Tasso's hell and the devil; who transforms Lucifer sometimes into a toad, and at others into a pygmy; who makes him say the same thing over again a hundred times; who metamorphoses him into a school-divine; and who, by an absurdly serious imitation of Ariosto's comic invention of firearms, represents the devils and angels cannonading each other in heaven? Neither I nor any other Italian can possibly take pleasure in such melancholy reveries; but the marriage of Sin and Death, and snakes issuing from the womb of the former, are enough to make any person sick that is not lost to all sense of delicacy. This obscene, eccentric, and disagreeable poem met with the neglect it deserved at its first publication; and I only treat the author now as he was treated in his own country by his contemporaries."

Candide was sensibly grieved at this speech, as he had a great respect for Homer, and was fond of Milton. "Alas!" said he softly to Martin, "I am afraid this man holds our German poets in great contempt." "There would be no such great harm in that," said Martin. "O what a surprising man!" said Candide, still to himself; "what a prodigious genius is this Pococuranté! nothing can please him."

After finishing their survey of the library, they went down into the garden, when Candide commended the several beauties that offered themselves to his view. "I know nothing upon earth laid out in such bad taste," said Pococuranté; "everything about it is childish and trifling; but I shall have another laid out to-morrow upon a nobler plan."

As soon as our two travellers had taken leave of his excellency, "Well," said Candide to Martin, "I hope you will own that this man is the happiest of all mortals, for he is above everything he possesses." "But do not you see," answered Martin, "that he likewise dislikes everything he possesses? It was an observation of Plato, long since, that those are not the best stomachs that reject, without distinction, all sorts of aliments." "True," said

---

[3] The Dominicans ran the Inquisition.

[4] Milton first published *Paradise Lost* in ten books in 1667; he divided it into twelve books in the second edition in 1674. Although an admirer of Milton, Voltaire became more and more critical of him in his later years.

Candide, "but still there must certainly be a pleasure in criticising everything, and in perceiving faults where others think they see beauties." "That is," replied Martin, "there is a pleasure in having no pleasure." "Well, well," said Candide, "I find that I shall be the only happy man at last, when I am blessed with the sight of my dear Cunégonde." "It is good to hope," said Martin.

In the meanwhile, days and weeks passed away, and no news of Cacambo. Candide was so overwhelmed with grief, that he did not reflect on the behavior of Pacquette and Friar Giroflée, who never stayed to return him thanks for the presents he had so generously made them.

Chapter XXVI.

CANDIDE AND MARTIN SUP WITH SIX FOREIGNERS—WHO THEY WERE.

One evening as Candide, with his attendant Martin, was going to sit down to supper with some foreigners who lodged in the same inn where they had taken up their quarters, a man with a face the color of soot came behind him, and taking him by the arm, said, "Hold yourself in readiness to go along with us; be sure you do not fail." Upon this, turning about to see from whom these words came, he beheld Cacambo. Nothing but the sight of Cunégonde could have given him greater joy and surprise. He was almost beside himself. After embracing this dear friend, "Cunégonde!" said he, is come with you doubtless! Where, where is she? Carry me to her this instant, that I may die with joy in her presence." "Cunégonde is not here," answered Cacambo; "she is in Constantinople." "Good heavens! in Constantinople! but no matter if she were in China, I would fly there. Quick, quick, dear Cacambo, let us be gone." "Soft and fair," said Cacambo, "stay till you have supped. I cannot at present stay to say anything more to you; I am a slave, and my master waits for me; I must go and attend him at table: but say not a word, only get your supper, and hold yourself in readiness."

Candide, divided between joy and grief, charmed to meet with his faithful agent again, and surprised to hear he was a slave, his heart palpitating, his senses confused, but full of the hopes of recovering his dear Cunégonde, sat down to table with Martin, who beheld all these scenes with great unconcern, and with six strangers, who had come to spend the carnival at Venice.

Cacambo waited at table upon one of those strangers. When supper was nearly over, he drew near to his master, and whispered in his ear, "Sir, your majesty may go when you please; the ship is ready"; and so saying he left the room. The guests, surprised at what they had heard, looked at each other without speaking a word; when another servant drawing near to his master, in like manner said, "Sir, your majesty's post-chaise is at Padua, and the ship is ready." The master made him a sign, and he instantly withdrew. The company all stared at each other again, and the general astonishment was increased. A third servant then approached another of the strangers, and said, "Sir, if your majesty will take my advice, you will not make any longer stay in this place; I will go and get everything ready"; and he instantly disappeared.

Candide and Martin then took it for granted that this was some of the diversions of the carnival, and that these were characters in masquerade. Then a fourth domestic said to the fourth stranger, "Your majesty may set off when you please"; saying which, he went away like the rest. A fifth valet said the same to a fifth master. But the sixth domestic spoke in a different style to the person on whom he waited, and who sat near to Candide. "Faith, sir," said he, "they will trust your majesty no longer, nor myself neither; and we may both of us chance to be sent to jail this very night; and therefore I shall take care of myself, and so adieu." The servants being all gone, the six strangers, with Candide and Martin, remained in a profound silence. At length Candide broke it by saying, "Gentlemen, this is a very singular joke upon my word; how came you all to be kings? For my part I admit that neither my friend Martin here, nor I, have any claim to royalty."

Cacambo's master then began, with great gravity, to speak in Italian. "I am not joking in the least, my name is Achmet III.[1] I was grand seignor for many years; I dethroned my brother, my nephew dethroned me, my viziers lost their heads, and I am condemned to end my days in the old seraglio. My nephew, the Grand Sultan Mahomet, gives me permission to travel sometimes for my health, and I have come to spend the carnival at Venice."

A young man who sat by Achmet, spoke next, and said: "My name is Ivan. I was once emperor of all the Russias, but was dethroned in my cradle. My parents were confined, and I was brought up in a prison, yet I am sometimes allowed to travel, though always with persons to keep a guard over me, and I have come to spend the carnival at Venice."

The third said: "I am Charles Edward, king of England; my father has renounced his right to the throne in my favor. I have fought in defence of my rights, and almost a thousand of my friends have had their hearts taken out of their bodies alive and thrown in their faces. I have myself been con-

---

[1] The list of kings mentioned is as follows: Achmet III (1673-1736); Ivan VI (1740-1764); "Bonnie Prince Charles, The Young Pretender" (1720-1788); Augustus III (1696-1763); Stanislas Leczinsky (1677-1766); Baron Neuhoff (1690-1765).

fined in a prison. I am going to Rome to visit the king my father, who was dethroned like me; and my grandfather and I have come to spend the carnival at Venice."

The fourth spoke thus: "I am the king of Poland; the fortune of war has stripped me of my hereditary dominions. My father experienced the same vicissitudes of fate. I resign myself to the will of Providence, in the same manner as Sultan Achmet, the Emperor Ivan, and King Charles Edward, whom God long preserve; and I have come to spend the carnival at Venice."

The fifth said: "I am king of Poland also. I have twice lost my kingdom; but Providence has given me other dominions, where I have done more good than all the Sarmatian kings put together were ever able to do on the banks of the Vistula; I resign myself likewise to Providence; and have come to spend the carnival at Venice."

It now came to the sixth monarch's turn to speak: "Gentlemen," said he, "I am not so great a prince as the rest of you, it is true, but I am, however, a crowned head. I am Theodore, elected king of Corsica. I have had the title of majesty, and am now hardly treated with common civility. I have coined money, and am not now worth a single ducat. I have had two secretaries, and am now without a valet. I was once seated on a throne, and since that have lain upon straw, in a common jail in London, and I very much fear I shall meet with the same fate here in Venice, where I came, like your majesties, to divert myself at the carnival."

The other five kings listened to this speech with great attention; it excited their compassion; each of them made the unhappy Theodore a present of twenty sequins, and Candide gave him a diamond, worth just a hundred times that sum. "Who can this private person be," said the five princes to one another, "who is able to give, and has actually given, a hundred times as much as any of us?"

Just as they rose from table, in came four serene highnesses, who had also been stripped of their territories by the fortune of war, and had come to spend the remainder of the carnival at Venice. Candide took no manner of notice of them; for his thoughts were wholly employed on his voyage to Constantinople, where he intended to go in search of his lovely Cunégonde.

Chapter XXVII.

CANDIDE'S VOYAGE TO CONSTANTINOPLE.

The trusty Cacambo had already engaged the captain of the Turkish ship that was to carry Sultan Achmet back to Constantinople, to take Candide and Martin on board. Accordingly they both embarked, after paying their obeisance to his miserable highness. As they were going on board, Candide said to Martin, "You see we supped in company with six dethroned kings, and to one of them I gave charity. Perhaps there may be a great many other princes still more unfortunate. For my part I have lost only a hundred sheep, and am now going to fly to the arms of my charming Cunégonde. My dear Martin, I must insist on it, that Pangloss was in the right. All is for the best." "I wish it may be," said Martin. "But this was an odd adventure we met with at Venice. I do not think there ever was an instance before of six dethroned monarchs supping together at a public inn." "This is not more extraordinary," said Martin, "than most of what has happened to us. It is a very common thing for kings to be dethroned; and as for our having the honor to eat with six of them, it is a mere accident, not deserving our attention."

As soon as Candide set his foot on board the vessel, he flew to his old friend and valet Cacambo; and throwing his arms about his neck, embraced him with joy. "Well," said he, "what news of Cunégonde? Does she still continue the paragon of beauty? Does she love me still? How does she do? You have, doubtless, purchased a superb palace for her at Constantinople."

"My dear master," replied Cacambo, "Cunégonde washes dishes on the banks of the Propontis, in the house of a prince who has very few to wash. She is at present a slave in the family of an ancient sovereign named Ragotski,[1] whom the grand Turk allows three crown a day to maintain him in his exile; but the most melancholy circumstance of all is, that she is turned horribly ugly." "Ugly or handsome," said Candide, "I am a man of honor; and, as such am obliged to love her still. But how could she possibly have been reduced to so abject a condition, when I sent five or six millions to her by you?" "Lord bless me," said Cacambo, "was not I obliged to give two millions to Señor Don Fernando d'Ibaraa y Fagueora y Mascarenes y Lampourdos y Souza, the governor of Buenos Aires, for liberty to take Cunégonde away with me? and then did not a brave fellow of a pirate gallantly strip us of all the rest? And then did not this same pirate carry us with him to Cape Matapan, to Milo, to Nicaria, to Samos, to Petra, to the Dardanelles, to Marmora, to Scutari? Cunégonde and the old woman are now servants to the prince I have told you of; and I myself am slave to the dethroned sultan." "What a chain of shocking accidents!" exclaimed Candide. "But after all, I have still some diamonds left, with which I can easily procure Cunégonde's liberty. It is a pity though she is grown so ugly."

Then turning to Martin, "What think you, friend," said he, "whose condition is most to be pitied, the Emperor Achmet's, the Emperor Ivan's, King

---

[1] King of Transylvania in 1707. He lost his throne and died in 1735.

Charles Edward's, or mine?" "I cannot resolve your question," said Martin, "unless I were in the hearts of you all." "Ah!" cried Candide, "was Pangloss here now, he would have known, and satisfied me at once." "I know not," said Martin, "in what balance your Pangloss could have weighed the misfortunes of mankind, and have set a just estimation on their sufferings. All that I pretend to know of the matter is that there are millions of men on the earth, whose conditions are a hundred times more pitiable than those of King Charles Edward, the Emperor Ivan, or Sultan Achmet." "Why, that may be," answered Candide.

In a few days they reached the Bosphorus; and the first thing Candide did was to pay a high ransom for Cacambo: then, without losing time, he and his companions went on board a galley, in order to search for his Cunégonde on the banks of the Propontis, despite the fact she had grown so ugly.

There were two slaves among the crew of the galley, who rowed very badly, and to whose bare backs the master of the vessel frequently applied a lash. Candide, from natural sympathy, looked at these two slaves more attentively than at any of the rest, and drew near them with an eye of pity. Their features, though greatly disfigured, appeared to him to bear a strong resemblance with those of Pangloss and the unhappy baron Jesuit, Cunégonde's brother. This idea affected him with grief and compassion: he examined them more attentively than before. "In truth," said he, turning to Martin, "if I had not seen my master Pangloss fairly hanged, and had not myself been unlucky enough to run my sword through the baron, I should absolutely think those two rowers were the men."

No sooner had Candide uttered the names of the baron and Pangloss, than the two slaves gave a great cry, ceased rowing, and let fall their oars out of their hands. The master of the vessel, seeing this, ran up to them, and redoubled the discipline of the lash. "Hold, hold," cried Candide, "I will give you what money you shall ask for these two persons." "Good heavens! it is Candide," said one of the men. "Candide!" cried the other. "Do I dream," said Candide, "or am I awake? Am I actually on board this galley? Is this my lord baron, whom I killed? and that my master Pangloss, whom I saw hanged before my face?"

"It is I! it is I!" cried they both together. "What! is this your great philosopher?" said Martin. "My dear sir," said Candide to the master of the galley, "how much do you ask for the ransom of the baron of Thunderten tronckh, who is one of the first barons of the empire, and of Pangloss, the most profound metaphysician in Germany?" "Why, then, Christian cur," replied the Turkish captain, "since these two dogs of Christian slaves are barons and metaphysicians, who no doubt are of high rank in their own country, you shall give me fifty thousand sequins." "You shall have them, sir; carry me back as quick as thought to Constantinople, and you shall receive the money immediately—No! carry me first to Cunégonde." The captain, upon Candide's first proposal, had already tacked about, and he made the crew ply their oars so effectually that the vessel flew through the water quicker than a bird cleaves the air.

Candide bestowed a thousand embraces on the baron and Pangloss. "And so then, my dear baron, I did not kill you? and you, my dear Pangloss, are come to life again after your hanging? But how came you slaves on board a Turkish galley?" "And is it true that my dear sister is in this country?" said the baron. "Yes," said Cacambo. "And do I once again behold my dear Candide?" said Pangloss. Candide presented Martin and Cacambo to them; they embraced each other, and all spoke together. The galley flew like lightning, and soon they got back to port. Candide instantly sent for a Jew, to whom he sold for fifty thousand sequins a diamond richly worth one hundred thousand, though the fellow swore to him all the time by Father Abraham that he gave him the most he could possibly afford. He no sooner got the money into his hands, than he paid it down for the ransom of the baron and Pangloss. The latter flung himself at the feet of his deliverer, and bathed him with his tears: the former thanked him with a gracious nod, and promised to return him the money the first opportunity. "But is it possible," said he, "that my sister is in Turkey?" "Nothing is more possible," answered Cacambo, "for she scours the dishes in the house of a Transylvanian prince." Candide sent directly for two Jews, and sold more diamonds to them; and then he set out with his companions in another galley, to deliver Cunégonde from slavery.

Chapter XXVIII.

WHAT BEFELL CANDIDE, CUNÉGONDE, PANGLOSS, MARTIN, ETC.

"Pardon," said Candide to the baron; "once more let me entreat your pardon, Reverend Father, for wounding you in the body." "Say no more about it," replied the baron; "I was a little too hasty I must admit; but as you seem to desire to know by what accident I came to be a slave on board the galley where you saw me, I will inform you. After I had been cured of the wound you gave me, by the college apothecary, I was attacked and carried off by a party of Spanish troops, who clapped me in prison in Buenos Aires, at the very time my sister was setting out from there. I asked leave to return to Rome, to the general of my order, who appointed me chaplain to the French ambassador at Constantinople. I had not been a week in my new office, when I happened to meet one evening with a young, extremely hand-some ichoglan.[1] The weather was very hot; the young man had an inclina-tion to bathe. I took the opportunity to bathe likewise. I did not know it was a crime for a Christian to be found naked in company with a young Turk. A cadi ordered me to receive a hundred blows on the soles of my feet, and sent me to the galleys. I do not believe that there was ever an act of more flagrant injustice. But I would like to know how my sister came to be a scullion to a Transylvanian prince, who has taken refuge among the Turks?"

"But how does it happen that I behold you again, my dear Pangloss?" said Candide. "It is true," answered Pangloss, "you saw me hanged, though I ought properly to have been burned; but you may remember, that it rained extremely hard when they were going to roast me. The storm was so violent that they found it impossible to light the fire; so they hanged me because they could do no better. A surgeon purchased my body, carried it home, and prepared to dissect me. He began by making a crucial incision from my navel to the clavicle. It is impossible for anyone to have been more poorly hanged than I had been. The executioner was a subdeacon, and knew how to burn people very well, but as for hanging, he was a novice at it, being quite out of practice; the cord being wet, and not slipping properly, the noose did not join. In short, I still continued to breathe; the crucial incision made me scream to such a degree that my surgeon fell flat upon his back; and imagining it was the devil he was dissecting, ran away, and in his fright tumbled down stairs. His wife hearing the noise, flew from the next room, and seeing me stretched upon the table with my crucial incision, was still more terrified than her husband, and fell upon him. When they had a little recovered themselves, I heard her say to her husband, 'My dear, how could you think of dissecting a heretic? Don't you know that the devil is always in them? I'll run directly to a priest to come and drive the evil spirit out.' I trembled from head to foot at hearing her talk in this manner, and exerted what little strength I had left to cry out, 'Have mercy on me!' At length the Portuguese barber[2] took courage, sewed up my wound, and his wife nursed me; and I was upon my legs in a fortnight's time. The barber got me a place to be lackey to a knight of Malta, who was going to Venice; but finding my master had no money to pay me my wages, I entered into the service of a Venetian merchant, and went with him to Constantinople.

"One day I happened to enter a mosque, where I saw no one but an old man and a very pretty young female devotee, who was telling her beads; her neck was quite bare, and in her bosom she had a beautiful nosegay of tulips, roses, anemones, buttercups, hyacinths, and auriculas; she let fall her nosegay. I ran immediately to take it up, and presented it to her with a most

---

[1] The page of a sultan.
[2] The surgeon.

respectful bow. I was so long in delivering it that the imam began to be angry; and, perceiving I was a Christian, he cried out for help; they carried me before the cadi, who ordered me to receive one hundred strokes, and sent me to the galleys. I was chained in the very galley and to the very same bench with the baron. On board this galley there were four young men belonging to Marseilles, five Neapolitan priests, and two monks of Corfu, who told us that similar adventures happened every day. The baron pretended that he had been worse used than myself; and I insisted that there was far less harm in taking up a nosegay, and putting it into a woman's bosom, than to be found stark naked with a young ichoglan. We were continually whipped, and received twenty lashes a day with a heavy thong, when the concatenation of earthly events brought you on board our galley to ransom us from slavery."

"Well, my dear Pangloss," said Candide to him, "when you were hanged, dissected, whipped, and tugging at the oar, did you continue to think that everything in this world happens for the best?" "I have always abided by my first opinion," answered Pangloss; "for, after all, I am a philosopher, and it would not become me to retract my sentiments, especially as Leibnitz could not be in the wrong: and that pre-established harmony is the finest thing in the world, as well as a *plenum* and the *materia subtilis.*"

Chapter XXIX.

IN WHAT MANNER CANDIDE FOUND CUNÉGONDE AND THE OLD WOMAN AGAIN.

While Candide, the baron, Pangloss, Martin, and Cacambo were relating their several adventures, and reasoning on the contingent or non-contingent events of this world, on causes and effects; on moral and physical evil, on free will and necessity, and on the consolation that may be felt by a person when a slave and chained to an oar in a Turkish galley, they arrived at the house of the Transylvanian prince on the coasts of the Propontis. The first objects they beheld there were Cunégonde and the old woman, who were hanging some tablecloths on a line to dry.

The baron turned pale at the sight. Even the tender Candide, that affectionate lover, upon seeing his fair Cunégonde, all sunburnt, with blear eyes, a withered neck, wrinkled face and arms, all covered with a red scurf, started back with horror; but, recovering himself, he advanced towards her out of good manners. She embraced Candide and her brother; they embraced the old woman, and Candide ransomed them both.

There was a small farm in the neighborhood, which the old woman proposed to Candide to use till the company should meet with a more favorable destiny. Cunégonde, not knowing that she had grown ugly, as no one had informed her of it, reminded Candide of his promise in so peremptory a manner that the simple lad did not dare to refuse her; he then told the baron that he was going to marry his sister. "I will never allow," said the baron, "my sister to be guilty of an action so derogatory to her birth and family; nor will I bear this insolence on your part: no, I never will be reproached that my nephews are not qualified for the first ecclesiastical dignities in Germany; nor shall a sister of mine ever be the wife of any person below the rank of a baron of the empire." Cunégonde flung herself at her brother's feet, and bathed them with tears; but he still continued inflexible. "You foolish fellow," said Candide, "have I not delivered you from the galleys, paid your ransom, and your sister's, too, who was a dish washer, and is very ugly, and yet condescended to marry her? And shall you pretend to oppose the match? If I were to listen only to the dictates of my anger, I would kill you again." "You may kill me again," said the baron; "but you shall not marry my sister while I am living."

Chapter XXX.

CONCLUSION.

Candide had, in truth, no great inclination to marry Cunégonde; but the extreme impertinence of the baron determined him to conclude the match; and Cunégonde pressed him so warmly that he could not recant. He consulted Pangloss, Martin, and the faithful Cacambo. Pangloss composed a fine memoir, by which he proved that the baron had no right over his sister; and that she might, according to all the laws of the empire, marry Candide with the left hand.[1] Martin concluded to throw the baron into the sea; Cacambo decided that he must be delivered to the Turkish captain and sent to the galleys, after which he should be conveyed by the first ship to the father-general at Rome. This advice was found to be good; the old woman approved of it, and not a syllable was said to his sister; the business was executed for a little money; and they had the pleasure of tricking a Jesuit and punishing the pride of a German baron.

It was altogether natural to imagine that after undergoing so many disasters, Candide, married to his mistress and living with the philosopher Pangloss, the philosopher Martin, the prudent Cacambo, and the old woman,

---

[1] A morganatic marriage in which the party with the lower rank would have no equality with the party of the higher rank.

having besides brought home so many diamonds from the country of the ancient Incas, would lead the most agreeable life in the world. But he had been so robbed by the Jews, that he had nothing left but his little farm; his wife, every day growing more and more ugly, became headstrong and insupportable; the old woman was infirm, and more ill-natured yet than Cunégonde. Cacambo, who worked in the garden, and carried the vegetables from it to sell at Constantinople, was above his labor, and cursed his fate. Pangloss despaired of making an impression in any of the German universities. And as for Martin, he was firmly persuaded that a person is equally ill-situated anywhere. He took things with patience. Candide, Martin, and Pangloss disputed sometimes about metaphysics and morality. Boats were often seen passing under the windows of the farm laden with effendis, bashaws, and cadis[2] that were going into banishment to Lemnos, Mitylene and Erzerum. And other cadis, bashaws, and effendis were seen coming back to succeed the place of the exiles, and were driven out in their turn. They saw several heads curiously stuck upon poles, and carried as presents to the Sublime Porte.[3] Such sights gave occasion to frequent dissertations; and when no disputes were in progress, the irksomeness was so excessive that the old woman ventured one day to tell them, "I would be glad to know which is worst, to be ravished a hundred times by Negro pirates, to have one buttock cut off, to run the gauntlet among the Bulgarians, to be whipped and hanged at an *auto-da-fé*, to be dissected, to be chained to an oar in a galley; and, in short, to experience all the miseries through which every one of us has passed or to remain here doing nothing?" "This," said Candide, "is a grand question."

This discourse gave birth to new reflections, and Martin especially concluded that man was born to live in the convulsions of anxiety or in the lethargy of idleness. Though Candide did not absolutely agree on this, yet he did not state an opinion. Pangloss avowed that he had undergone dreadful sufferings; but having once maintained that everything went on as well as possible, he still maintained it, and at the same time believed nothing of it.

There was one thing which more than ever confirmed Martin in his detestable principles, made Candide hesitate, and embarrassed Pangloss: the arrival of Pacquette and Brother Giroflée one day at their farm. This couple had been in the utmost distress; they had very speedily made away with their three thousand piastres; they had parted, been reconciled; quarrelled again, been thrown into prison; had made their escape, and at last Brother Giroflée had turned Turk. Pacquette still continued to follow her trade; but she got little or nothing by it. "I foresaw very well,"

---

[2] Turkish civil and military officials.
[3] The gate of the Sultan's palace where once justice was administered.

said Martin to Candide, "that your presents would soon be squandered, and only make them more miserable. You and Cacambo have spent millions of piastres, and yet you are not more happy than Brother Giroflée and Pacquette." "Ah!" said Pangloss to Pacquette, "it is heaven that has brought you here among us, my poor child! Do you know that you have cost me the tip of my nose, one eye, and one ear? What a handsome shape is here! And what is this world!" This new adventure engaged them more deeply than ever in philosophical disputations.

In the neighborhood lived a famous dervish who passed for the best philosopher in Turkey; they went to consult him: Pangloss, who was their spokesman, addressed him thus: "Master, we come to ask you to tell us why so strange an animal as man has been formed."

"Why do you trouble your head about it?" said the dervish; "is it any business of yours?" "But, my reverend father," said Candide, "there is a great deal of evil on earth." "What signifies it," said the dervish, "whether there is evil or good? When his highness sends a ship to Egypt does he trouble his head whether the rats in the vessel are at their ease or not?" "What must then be done?" said Pangloss. "Be silent," answered the dervish. "I flattered myself," replied Pangloss, "to have reasoned a little with you on the causes and effects, on the best of possible worlds, the origin of evil, the nature of the soul, and a pre-established harmony." At these words the dervish shut the door in their faces.

During this conversation, news was spread abroad that two viziers[4] of the bench and the mufti[5] had just been strangled at Constantinople, and several of their friends empaled. This catastrophe made a great stir for some hours. Pangloss, Candide, and Martin, as they were returning to the little farm, met with a good-looking old man, who was taking the air at his door, under an alcove formed of the boughs of orange-trees. Pangloss, who was as inquisitive as he was disputative, asked him what was the name of the mufti who was lately strangled. "I cannot tell," answered the good old man; "I never knew the name of any mufti, or vizier breathing. I am entirely ignorant of the event you speak of; I presume that in general such as are concerned in public affairs sometimes come to a miserable end; and that they deserve it: but I never inquire what is doing at Constantinople; I am contented with sending there the produce of my garden, which I cultivate with my own hands." After saying these words, he invited the strangers to come into his house. His two daughters and two sons presented them with various sorts of sherbet of their own making; besides caymac, heightened with the peels of candied citrons, oranges, lemons, pineapples, pistachio

---

[4] Prime ministers.
[5] An official expounder of Mohammedan law.

nuts, and Mocha coffee unadulterated with the bad coffee of Batavia or the West Indies. After which the two daughters of this good Mussulman perfumed the beards of Candide, Pangloss, and Martin.

"You must certainly have a vast estate," said Candide to the Turk, who replied, "I have no more than twenty acres of ground, the whole of which I cultivate myself with the help of my children; and our labor keeps off from us three great evils—idleness, vice, and want."

Candide, as he was returning home, made profound reflections on the Turk's discourse. "This good old man," he said to Pangloss and Martin, "appears to me to have chosen for himself a lot much preferable to that of the six kings with whom we had the honor to dine." "Human grandeur," said Pangloss, "is very dangerous, if we believe the testimonies of almost all philosophers; for we find Eglon, king of Moab, was assassinated by Aod; Absalom was hanged by the hair of his head, and run through with three darts; King Nadab, son of Jeroboam, was slain by Baaza; King Ela by Zimri; Okosias by Jehu; Athaliah by Jehoiada; the kings Jehooiakim, Jeconiah, and Zedekiah, were led into captivity: I need not tell you what was the fate of Croesus, Astyages, Darius, Dionysius of Syracuse, Pyrrhus, Perseus, Hannibal, Jugurtha, Ariovistus, Caesar, Pompey, Nero, Otho, Vitellius, Domitian, Richard II. of England, Edward II., Henry VI., Richard III., Mary Stuart, Charles I., the three Henrys of France, and the emperor Henry IV." "Neither need you tell me," said Candide, "that we must take care of our garden." "You are in the right," said Pangloss; "for when man was put into the garden of Eden, it was with an intent to toil there: and this proves that man was not born to be idle." "Work then without disputing," said Martin; "it is the only way to render life supportable."

The little society, one and all, entered into this laudable plan and began to exert their different talents. The little piece of ground yielded them a plentiful crop. Cunégonde indeed was very ugly, but she became an excellent hand at pastrywork; Pacquette embroidered; the old woman had the care of the linen. There was none, down to Brother Giroflée, who failed to perform some service; he was a very good carpenter, and became an honest man. Pangloss used now and then to say to Candide, "There is a concatenation of all events in the best of possible worlds; for, in short, had you not been kicked out of a fine castle for the love of Cunégonde; had you not been put into the Inquisition; had you not travelled over America on foot; had you not run the sword through the baron; and had you not lost all your sheep, which you brought from the good country of El Dorado, you would not have been here to eat preserved citrons and pistachio nuts." "Excellently observed," answered Candide; "but let us cultivate our garden."

Questions for Discussion

1. What is the philosophy of the tutor Pangloss that Voltaire is satirizing? To what extent is Candide in the beginning the embodiment of this philosophy? Is Voltaire satirizing Candide's character or his education?

2. What is the significance of the Lisbon earthquake for Pangloss and Candide?

3. Contrast the appearance of Cunégonde at the beginning and at the end of the story. What point does Voltaire make with this contrast?

4. Of the various aspects of society Voltaire satirizes such as religious fanaticism, slavery, war, tyranny, racial discrimination, which do you think he stresses the most?

5. Is El Dorado held up as an utopian society in comparison with the other countries Candide travels through? How, for instance, does its religion differ from that of other countries he visits? To what extent is it like the model society of the garden mentioned at the end of the book?

6. How is the philosophy of Martin opposed to that of Pangloss? How is it opposed to Candide's?

7. Do Pangloss, Candide, and Martin change their ideas at the end of the story? Do they agree with the Turk on cultivating their own gardens? Do you think the Turk's position is Voltaire's? If so, why?

8. From what intellectual position does Voltaire seem to ridicule mankind? Is he a skeptic, optimist, rationalist, idealist, realist, a combination of several of these, or something else?

9. To what extent do you think Voltaire is satirizing romantic travel books about remote and exotic countries?

10. Explain how irony is used in presenting one of Candide's adventures.

Robert Burns (1759-1796)

Holy Willie's Prayer[1]

O Thou that in the Heavens does dwell,
Wha, as it pleases best Thysel,
Sends ane to Heaven an' ten to Hell
      A' for Thy glory,
And no for onie guid or ill
        They've done before Thee!

I bless and praise Thy matchless might,
When thousands Thou hast left in night,
That I am here before Thy sight,
      For gifts an' grace   10
A burning and a shining light
        To a' this place.

What was I, or my generation,
That I should get sic exaltation?
I, wha deserv'd most just damnation
      For broken laws
Sax thousand years ere my creation,
        Thro' Adam's cause!

When from my mither's womb I fell,
Thou might hae plung'd me deep in hell   20
To gnash my gooms, and weep, and wail
      In burning lakes,
Whare damnéd devils roar and yell,
        Chain'd to their stakes.

---

[1] Holy Willie was in real life William Fisher, a Presbyterian Elder, who upheld the Calvinist doctrine of predestination and election. Before the Presbytery of Ayr he charged Gavin Hamilton, a man of good character, with immoral conduct. Robert Aiken successfully defended the accused man.

Yet I am here, a chosen sample,
To show Thy grace is great and ample:
I'm here a pillar o' Thy temple,
   Strong as a rock,
A guide, a buckler,[2] and example
   To a' Thy flock!   30

O Lord, Thou kens what zeal I bear,
When drinkers drink, and swearers swear,
And singin there and dancin here,
   Wi' great an' sma':
For I am keepit by Thy fear,
   Free frae them a'.

But yet, O Lord! confess I must:
At times I'm fash'd[3] wi' fleshly lust;
An' sometimes, too, in warldly trust,
   Vile self gets in;   40
But Thou remembers we are dust,
   Defiled wi' sin.

O Lord! yestreen,[4] Thou kens,[5] wi' Meg—
Thy pardon I sincerely beg—
O, may't ne'er be a living plague
   To my dishonour!
An' I'll ne'er lift a lawless leg
   Again upon her.

Besides, I farther maun[6] avow—
Wi' Leezie's lass, three times, I trow—   50
But, Lord, that Friday I was fou,[7]
   When I cam near her,
Or else, Thou kens, Thy servant true
   Wad never steer[8] her.

---

2 Defender.
3 Troubled.
4 Last night.
5 Knowest.
6 Must.
7 Drunk.
8 Meddle with.

Maybe Thou lets this fleshly thorn
Buffet Thy servant e'en and morn,
Lest he owre proud and high should turn
      That he's sae gifted:
If sae, Thy han' maun e'en be borne
      Until Thou lift it.   60

Lord, bless Thy chosen in this place,
For here Thou has a chosen race!
But God confound their stubborn face
      An' blast their name,
Wha bring Thy elders to disgrace
      An' open shame!

Lord, mind Gau'n Hamilton's deserts:
He drinks, an' swears, an' plays at cartes,
Yet has sae monie takin arts
      Wi' great and sma',   70
Frae God's ain Priest the people's hearts
      He steals awa.

And when we chasten'd him therefore
Thou kens how he bred sic a splore,[9]
And set the warld in a roar
      O' laughin at us:
Curse Thou his basket and his store,
      Kail[10] an' potatoes!

Lord, hear my earnest cry and pray'r
Against that Presbyt'ry of Ayr!   80
Thy strong right hand, Lord, mak it bare
      Upo' their heads!
Lord, visit them, an' dinna spare,
      For their misdeeds!

O Lord, my God! that glib-tongu'd Aiken,
My vera heart and flesh are quakin

---

[9] Such a row.
[10] Broth.

To think how we stood sweatin, shakin,
     An' pish'd wi' dread,
While he, wi' hingin[11] lip an' snakin,[12]
     Held up his head.   90

Lord, in Thy day o' vengeance try him!
Lord, visit him wha did employ him!
And pass not in Thy mercy by them,
     Nor hear their pray'r,
But for Thy people's sake destroy them,
     An' dinna spare!

But, Lord, remember me and mine
Wi' mercies temporal and divine,
That I for grace an' gear[13] may shine
     Excell'd by nane;   100
And a' the glory shall be Thine—
     Amen, Amen.

Questions for Discussion

1. Why is the satire of Willie put in the form of a prayer? Is the language appropriate for a prayer?

2. How does Willie rationalize his sins? What are these sins?

3. To what extent is the satire concerned with more than Willie? Where in particular is this broader satire evident?

4. How is Willie's attack on his enemies an unintentional damnation of himself?

5. What is Willie seeking of the Lord in the last stanza?

---

[11] Hanging.
[12] Sneering.
[13] Wealth.

William Blake (1757-1827)

London

I wander through each chartered[1] street,
Near where the chartered Thames does flow,
And mark in every face I meet
Marks of weakness, marks of woe.

In every cry of every Man,
In every Infant's cry of fear,
In every voice, in every ban,[2]
The mind-forged manacles I hear.

How the Chimney-sweeper's cry
Every blackening Church appalls;
And the hapless Soldier's sigh
Runs in blood down Palace walls.

But most through midnight streets I hear
How the youthful Harlot's curse
Blasts the new born Infant's tear,
And blights with plagues the Marriage hearse.

---

[1] "Chartered" has two meanings: laid out and rented out.
[2] Curse.

Questions for Discussion

1. Is the poet attacking London, the social and political system of the time, or something else?

2. What are the "mind-forged manacles" mentioned in stanza two?

3. Why are "chartered" and "mark" repeated in the first stanza?

4. Explain the two main images in stanza three. In what way are the soot blackening the church and the blood staining the palace alike?

5. Why is the "Harlot's curse" the most terrible cry the speaker hears in London?

6. Explain the paradox of "Marriage hearse." To what extent is it satirical and to what extent is it not?

John Betjeman (1906-   )

In Westminster Abbey

Let me take this other glove off
  As the *vox humana*[1] swells,
And the beauteous fields of Eden
  Bask beneath the Abbey bells.
Here, where England's statesmen lie,
Listen to a lady's cry.

Gracious Lord, oh bomb the Germans.
  Spare their women for Thy Sake,
And if that is not too easy
  We will pardon Thy Mistake.   10
But, gracious Lord, whate'er shall be,
Don't let anyone bomb me.

Keep our Empire undismembered
  Guide our Forces by Thy Hand,
Gallant blacks from far Jamaica,
  Honduras and Togoland;
Protect them Lord in all their fights,
And, even more, protect the whites.

Think of what our Nation stands for,
  Books from Boots'[2] and country lanes,   20
Free speech, free passes, class distinction,
  Democracy and proper drains.
Lord, put beneath Thy special care
One-eighty-nine Cadogan Square.

"In Westminster Abbey" by John Betjeman. Reprinted with permission of John Murray from *Collected Poems* by John Betjeman.

[1] An organ stop that makes tones similar to those of the human voice.
[2] A famous pharmacy which includes a rental library.

Although dear Lord I am a sinner,
  I have done no major crime;
Now I'll come to Evening Service
  Whensoever I have time.
So, Lord, reserve for me a crown,
And do not let my shares go down.   30

I will labour for Thy Kingdom,
  Help our lads to win the war,
Send white feathers to the cowards
  Join the Women's Army Corps,
Then wash the Steps around Thy Throne
In the Eternal Safety Zone.

Now I feel a little better,
  What a treat to hear Thy Word,
Where the bones of leading statesmen,
  Have so often been interr'd.   40
And now, dear Lord, I cannot wait
Because I have a luncheon date.

Questions for Discussion

1. To what extent is the satire of religious hypocrisy in this poem similar to that in "Holy Willie's Prayer"?

2. What is the speaker's attitude toward her country? How would you define her kind of patriotism?

3. What does the speaker mean at the beginning of the last stanza when she says, "Now I feel a little better"?

4. The last line of each stanza serves a similar function. What is it? Explain the appropriateness of the last line of the poem as a fitting end to the prayer.

5. How does the setting of Westminster Abbey during World War II heighten the satire? Is the language of the poem in keeping with the solemn environment?

J. F. Powers (1917-   )

Blue Island

On the day Daviccis moved into their house, Ethel was visited by a "Welcome Wagon" hostess bearing small gifts from local merchants, but after that by nobody for three weeks, only Ralph's relatives and door-to-door salesmen. And then Mrs. Hancock came smiling. They sat on the matching green chairs which glinted with threads of what appeared to be gold. In the picture window, the overstimulated plants grew wild in pots.

Mrs. Hancock had guessed right about Ethel and Ralph, that they were newlyweds. "Am I right in thinking you're of Swedish descent, Mrs. Davicky? You, I mean?"

Ethel smiled, as if taking a compliment, and said nothing.

"I only ask because so many people in the neighborhood are. I'm not, myself," said Mrs. Hancock. She was unnaturally pink, with tinted blue hair. Her own sharp-looking teeth were transparent at the tips. "But you're so fair."

"My maiden name was Taylor," Ethel said. It was, and it wasn't—it was the name she'd got at the orphanage. Wanting a cigarette, she pushed the silver box on the coffee table toward Mrs. Hancock.

Mrs. Hancock used one of her purple claws to pry up the first cigarette from the top layer. "A good old American name like mine."

Like *what?* Ethel wanted to ask. Mrs. Hancock wasn't giving her maiden name, though.

"Is your husband in business, Mrs. Davicky?"

"Yes, he is." Ethel put the lighter—a simple column of silver, the mate to the box—to Mrs. Hancock's cigarette and then to her own.

"Not here in Blue Island?"

"No." From here on, it could be difficult. Ralph was afraid that people in the neighborhood would disapprove of his business. "In Minneapolis." The Mohawk Inn, where Ethel had worked as a waitress, was first-class—thick steaks, dark lights, an electric organ—but Ralph's other places, for which his brothers were listed as the owners, were cut-rate bars on or near Washington Avenue. "He's a distributor," Ethel said, heading her off. "Non-alcoholic beverages mostly." It was true. Ralph had taken over his family's wholesale wine business, never much in Minneapolis, and got it to pay by converting to soft drinks.

Mrs. Hancock was noticing the two paintings which, because of their size and the lowness of the ceiling, hung two feet from the floor, but she didn't comment on them. "Lovely, lovely," she said, referring to the driftwood lamp in the picture window. A faraway noise came from her stomach. She raised her voice. "But you've been lonely, haven't you? I could see it when I came in. It's this neighborhood."

"It's very nice," said Ethel quickly. Maybe Mrs. Hancock was at war with the neighbors, looking for an ally.

"I suppose you know Mrs. Nilgren," said Mrs. Hancock, nodding to the left.

"No, but I've seen her. Once she waved."

"She's nice. Tied down with children, though." Mrs. Hancock nodded to the right. "How about old Mrs. Mann?"

"I don't think anybody's there now."

"The Manns are away! California. So you don't know anybody yet?"

"No."

"I'm surprised you haven't met some of them at the Cashway."

"I never go there," Ethel said. "Ralph—that's my husband—he wants me to trade at the home-owned stores."

"Oh?" Mrs. Hancock's stomach cut loose again. "I didn't know people still felt that way." Mrs. Hancock looked down the street, in the direction of the little corner store. "Do they do much business?"

"No," said Ethel. The old couple who ran it were suspicious of her, she thought, for buying so much from them. The worst of it was that Ralph had told her to open a charge account, and she hadn't, and she never knew when he'd stop there and try to use it. There was a sign up in the store that said: In God We Trust—All Others Pay Cash.

"I'll bet that's it," Mrs. Hancock was saying. "I'm afraid people are pretty clannish around here—and the Wagners have so many friends. They live one-two-three-five houses down." Mrs. Hancock had been counting the houses across the street. "Mr. Wagner's the manager of the Cashway."

Ethel was holding her breath.

"I'm afraid so," said Mrs. Hancock.

Ethel sighed. It was Ralph's fault. She'd always wanted to trade at the Cashway.

Mrs. Hancock threw back her head, inhaling, and her eyelids, like a doll's, came down. "I'm afraid it's your move, Mrs. Davicky."

Ethel didn't feel that it was her move at all and must have shown it.

Mrs. Hancock sounded impatient. "Invite 'em in. Have 'em in for a morning coffee."

"I couldn't do that," Ethel said. "I've never been to one." She'd only read about coffees in the women's magazines to which Ralph subscribed her. "I wouldn't know how."

"Nothing to it. Rolls, coffee, and come as you are. Of course nobody really does, not really." Mrs. Hancock's stomach began again. "Oh, shut up," she said to it. "I've just come from one too many." Mrs. Hancock made a face, showing Ethel a brown mohair tongue. She laughed at Ethel. "Cheer up. It wasn't in this neighborhood."

Ethel felt better. "I'll certainly think about it," she said.

Mrs. Hancock rose, smiling, and went over to the telephone. "You'll do it right now," she said, as though being an older woman entitled her to talk that way to Ethel. "They're probably dying to get inside this lovely house."

After a moment, Ethel, who was already on her feet, having thought that Mrs. Hancock was leaving, went over and sat down to telephone. In the wall mirror she saw how she must appear to Mrs. Hancock. When the doorbell had rung, she'd been in too much of a hurry to see who it was to do anything about her lips and hair. "Will they know who I am?"

"Of course." Mrs. Hancock squatted on the white leather hassock with the phone book. "And you don't have to say I'm coming. Oh, I'll come. I'll be more than happy to. You don't need me, though. All you need is confidence."

And Mrs. Hancock was right. Ethel called eight neighbors, and six could come on Wednesday morning, which Mrs. Hancock had thought would be the best time for her. Two of the six even sounded anxious to meet Ethel, and, surprisingly, Mrs. Wagner was one of these.

"You did it all yourself," said Mrs. Hancock.

"With your help," said Ethel, feeling indebted to Mrs. Hancock, intimately so. It was as if they'd cleaned the house together.

They were saying goodbye on the front stoop when Ralph rolled into the driveway. Ordinarily at noon he parked just outside the garage, but that day he drove in—without acknowledging them in any way. "Mr. Daveechee," Ethel commented. For Mrs. Hancock, after listening to Ethel pronounce her name for all the neighbors, was still saying "Davicky."

Mrs. Hancock stayed long enough to get the idea that Ralph wasn't going to show himself. She went down the front walk saying, " 'Bye now."

While Mrs. Hancock was getting into her car, which seemed a little old for the neighborhood, Ralph came out of the garage.

Mrs. Hancock waved and nodded—which, Ethel guessed, was for Ralph's benefit, the best Mrs. Hancock could do to introduce herself at the distance. She drove off. Too late, Ralph's hand moved up to wave. He stared after Mrs. Hancock's moving car with a look that just didn't belong to him, Ethel thought, a look that she hadn't seen on his face until they moved out to Blue Island.

During lunch, Ethel tried to reproduce her conversation with Mrs. Hancock, but she couldn't tell Ralph enough. He wanted to know the neighbors' names, and she could recall the names of only three. Mrs. Wagner, one of them, was very popular in the neighborhood, and her husband . . . "You go to the Cashway then. Some of 'em sounded all right, huh?" "Ralph, they all sounded all right, real friendly. The man next door sells insurance. Mr. Nilgren."

Ethel remembered that one of the husbands was a lawyer and told Ralph that. He left the table. A few minutes later, Ethel heard him driving away.

It had been a mistake to mention the lawyer to Ralph. It had made him think of the shooting they'd had at the Bow Wow, one of the joints. There had been a mixup, and Ralph's home address had appeared in the back pages of one of the papers when the shooting was no longer news. Ethel doubted that the neighbors had seen the little item. Ralph might be right about the lawyer, though, who would probably have to keep up with everything like that.

Ralph wouldn't have worried so much about such a little thing in the old days. He was different now. It was hard to get him to smile. Ethel could remember how he would damn the Swedes for slapping higher and higher taxes on liquor and tobacco, but now, when she pointed out a letter some joker had written to the paper suggesting a tax on coffee, or when she showed him the picture of the wife of the Minnesota senator—the fearless one—christening an ore boat with a bottle of milk, which certainly should've given Ralph a laugh, he was silent.

It just made Ethel sick to see him at the windows, watching Mr. Nilgren, a sandy-haired, dim-looking man who wore plaid shirts and a red cap in the yard. Mr. Nilgren would be raking out his hedge, or wiring up the skinny little trees, or washing his car if it was Sunday morning, and there Ralph would be, behind a drape. One warm day Ethel had seen Mr. Nilgren in the yard with a golf club, and had said, "He should get some of those little balls that don't go anywhere." It had been painful to see Ralph then. She could almost *hear* him thinking. He would get some of those balls and give them to Mr. Nilgren as a present. No, it would look funny if he did. Then he got that sick look that seemed to come from wanting to do a favor for someone who might not let him do it.

A couple of days later Ethel learned that Ralph had gone to an indoor driving range to take golf lessons. He came home happy, with a club he was supposed to swing in his spare time. He'd made a friend too, another beginner. They were going to have the same schedule and be measured for clubs. During his second lesson, however, he quit. Ethel wasn't surprised, for Ralph, though strong, was awkward. She was better than he was with a hammer and nails, and he mutilated the heads of screws. He must have been badly surprised to discover he was just as bad when he went back the second time, after carrying the club around the house for three days. Ethel asked about the other beginner, and at first Ralph acted as though she'd made him up, and then he hotly rejected the word "friend," which she'd used. Finally he said, "If you ask me, that bastard's played before!"

That was just like him. At the coffee, Ethel planned to ask the women to come over soon with their husbands, but she was afraid some of the husbands wouldn't take to Ralph. Probably he could buy insurance from Mr. Nilgren. He would want to do something for the ones who weren't selling something, though—if there were any like that—and they might misunderstand Ralph. He was used to buying the drinks. He should relax and take the neighbors as they came. Or move.

She didn't know why they were there anyway. It was funny. After they were married, before they left their honeymoon, Ralph had driven her out to Blue Island and walked her through the house. That was all there was to it. Sometimes she wondered if he'd won the house at cards. She didn't know why they were there when they could just as well be living at Minnetonka or White Bear where they could keep a launch like the one they'd hired in Florida—and where the houses were far apart and neighbors wouldn't matter so much. What were they waiting for? Some of the things they owned, she knew, were for later. They didn't need sterling for eighteen in Blue Island. And the two big pictures were definitely for later.

She didn't know what Ralph liked about his picture, which was of an Indian who looked all-in sitting on a horse that looked all-in, but he had gone to the trouble of ordering it from a regular art store. Hers was more cheerful, the palace of the Doge of Venice, Italy. Ralph hadn't wanted her to have it at first. He was really down on anything foreign. (There were never any Italian dishes on the menu at the Mohawk.) But she believed he liked her for wanting that picture, for having a weakness for things Italian, for him—and even for his father and mother whom he was always sorry to see and hadn't invited to the house. When they came anyway, with his brothers, their wives and children (and wine, which Ralph wouldn't touch), Ralph was in and out, upstairs and down, never long in the same room with them, never encouraging them to stay when they started to leave. They called him "Rock" or "Rocky," but Ralph didn't always answer to that. To one of the little boys who had followed him down into the basement, Ethel had heard him growl, "The name's Ralph"—that to a nine-year-old. His family must have noticed the change in Ralph, but they were wrong if they blamed her, just because she was a little young for him, a blonde and not a Catholic—not that Ralph went to church. In fact, she thought Ralph would be better off with his family for his friends, instead of counting so much on the neighbors. She liked Ralph's family and enjoyed having them in the house.

And if Ralph's family hadn't come around, the neighbors might even think they weren't properly married, that they had a love nest going there. Ethel didn't blame the neighbors for being suspicious of her and Ralph. Mr. Nilgren in his shirt and cap that did nothing for him, he belonged there, but not Ralph, so dark, with his dark blue suits, pearl grey hats, white jacquard shirts—and with her, with her looks and platinum hair. She tried to dress down, to look like an older woman, when she went out. The biggest thing in their favor, but it wasn't noticeable yet, was the fact that she was pregnant.

Sometimes she thought Ralph must be worrying about the baby—as she was—about the kind of life a little kid would have in a neighborhood where his father and mother didn't know anybody. There were two pre-school children at the Nilgrens'. Would they play with the Davicci kid? Ethel didn't ever want to see that sick look of Ralph's on a child of hers.

That afternoon two men in white overalls arrived from Minneapolis in a white truck and washed the windows, inside and out, including the basement and garage. Ralph had sent them. Ethel sat in the dining room and polished silver to the music of *Carmen* on records. She played whole operas when Ralph wasn't home.

In bed that night Ralph made her run through the neighbors again. Seven for sure, counting Mrs. Hancock. "Is that all?" Ethel said she was going to call the neighbor who hadn't been home. "When?" When she got the number from Mrs. Hancock. "When's that?" When Mrs. Hancock phoned, if she phoned . . . and that was where Ralph believed Ethel had really fallen down. She didn't have Mrs. Hancock's number—or address—and there wasn't a Hancock listed for Blue Island in the phone book. "How about next door?" Mrs. Nilgren was still coming. "The other side?" The Manns were still away, in California, and Ralph knew it. "They might come back. Ever think of that? You don't wanna leave them out." *Them,* he'd said, showing Ethel what was expected of her. He wanted those hus-bands. Ethel promised to watch for the return of the Manns. "They could come home in the night." Ethel reminded Ralph that a person in her condition needed a lot of sleep, and Ralph left her alone then.

Before Ralph was up the next morning, Ethel started to clean the house. Ralph was afraid the house-cleaning wouldn't be done right (*he* spoke of her condition) and wanted to get another crew of professionals out from Minneapolis. Ethel said it wouldn't look good. She said the neighbors expected them to do their own house-cleaning—*and window washing*. Ralph shut up.

When he came home for lunch, Ethel was able to say that Mrs. Hancock had called and that the neighbor who hadn't been home could come to the coffee. Ethel had talked to her, and she sounded very friendly. "That's three of 'em, huh?" Ethel was tired of that one, but told him they'd *all* sounded friendly to her. "Mrs. Hancock okay?" Mrs. Hancock was okay. More than happy to be coming. Ralph asked if Ethel had got Mrs. Hancock's phone number and address. No. "Why not?" Mrs. Hancock would be there in the morning. That was why—and Ralph should get a hold on himself.

In the afternoon, after he was gone, Ethel put on one of her new conservative dresses and took the bus to Minneapolis to buy some Swedish pastry. She wanted something better than she could buy in Blue Island. In the window of the store where they'd bought Ralph's Indian, there were some little miniatures, lovely New England snow scenes. She hesitated to go in when she saw the sissy clerk was on duty again. He had made Ralph sore, asking how he'd like to have the Indian framed in birch bark. The Mohawk was plastered with birch bark, and Ralph thought the sissy recognized him and was trying to be funny. "This is going into my home!" Ralph had said and ordered the gold frame costing six times as much as the Indian. However, he'd taken the sissy's advice about having a light up on it. Ethel hesitated, but she went in. In his way, the sissy was very nice, and Ethel went home with five little Old English prints. When she'd asked about the pictures in the window, the New England ones, calling them "landscapes," he'd said "snowscapes" and looked disgusted, as if they weren't what she should want.

When she got home, she hung the prints over the sofa where there was a blank space, and they looked fine in their shiny black frames. She didn't say anything to Ralph, hoping he'd notice them, but he didn't until after supper. "Hey, what is this?" he said. He bounced off the sofa, confronting her. "Ralph, they're cute!" "Not in my home!" "Ralph, they're humorous!" The clerk had called them that. But Ralph called them drunks and whores. He had Ethel feeling ashamed of herself. It was hard to believe that she could have felt they were just fat and funny and just what their living room needed, as the clerk had said. Ralph took them down. "Man or woman sell 'em to you?" Ethel, seeing what he had in mind, knew she couldn't tell him where she'd got them. She lied. "I was in Dayton's . . ." "A woman—all right, then you take 'em back!"

She was scared. Something like that was enough to make Ralph regret *marrying* her—and to remind her again that she couldn't have made him. If there had been a showdown between them, he would've learned about her first pregnancy. It would've been easy for a lawyer to find out about that. She'd listened to an old doctor who'd told her to go ahead and have it, that she'd love her little baby, who hadn't lived, but there would be a record anyway. She wasn't sorry about going to a regular hospital to have it, though it made it harder for her now, having that record. She'd done what she could for the baby. She hated to think of the whole thing, but when she did, as she did that evening, she knew she'd done her best.

It might have been a bad evening for her, with Ralph brooding on her faults, if a boy hadn't come to the door selling chances on a raffle. Ralph bought all the boy had, over five dollars' worth, and asked where he lived in the neighborhood. "I live in Minneapolis." "Huh? Whatcha doin' way out here then?" The boy said it was easier to sell chances out there. Ethel, who had been doing the dishes, returned to the sink before Ralph could see her. He went back to his *Reader's Digest*, and she slipped off to bed, early, hoping his mind would be occupied with the boy if she kept out of sight.

He came to bed after the ten o'clock news. "You awake?" Ethel, awake, but afraid he wanted to talk neighbors, moaned remotely. "If anybody comes to the door sellin' anything, make sure it's somebody local."

In the morning, Ralph checked over the silver and china laid out in the dining room and worried over the pastry. "Fresh?" Fresh! She'd put it in the deep freeze right away and it hadn't even thawed out yet. "Is *that* all?" That was all, and it was more than enough. She certainly didn't need a whole quart of whipping cream. "Want me to call up for something to go with this?" No. "Turkey or a ham? I maybe got time to go myself if I go right now." He carried on like that until ten o'clock, when she got rid of him, saying, "You wouldn't want to be the only man, Ralph."

Then she was on her own, wishing Mrs. Hancock would come early and see her through the first minutes.

But Mrs. Wagner was the first to arrive. After that, the neighbors seemed to ring the bell at regular intervals. Ethel met them at the door, hung their coats in the hall closet, returning each time to Mrs. Wagner in the kitchen. They were all very nice, but Mrs. Wagner was the nicest.

"Now let's just let everything be," she said after they'd arranged the food in the dining room. "Let's go in and meet your friends."

They found the neighbors standing before the two pictures. Ethel snapped on the spot lights. She heard little cries of pleasure all around.

"Heirlooms!"

"Is Mr. Davitchy a collector?"

"Just likes good things, huh?"

"I just love this lamp."

"I just *stare* at it when I go by."

"So do I."

Ethel, looking at her driftwood lamp, her plants, and beyond, stood in a haze of pleasure. Earlier, when she was giving her attention to Mrs. Nilgren (who was telling about the trouble "Carl" had with his trees), Ethel had seen Ralph's car cruise by, she thought, and now again, but this time there was no doubt of it. She recognized the rather old one parked in front as Mrs. Hancock's, but where was Mrs. Hancock?

"Hello, everybody!"

Mrs. Hancock had let herself in, and was hanging up her coat.

Ethel disappeared into the kitchen. She carried the coffee pot, which had been on *low*, into the dining room where they were supposed to come and help themselves. She stood by the pot, nervous, ready to pour, hoping that someone would look in and see that she was ready, but no one did.

She went to see what they were doing. They were still sitting down, listening to Mrs. Hancock. She'd had trouble with her car. That was why she was late. She saw Ethel. "I can see you want to get started," she said, rising. "So do I."

Ethel returned to the dining room and stood by the coffee pot.

Mrs. Hancock came first. "Starved," she said. She carried off her coffee, roll, and two of the little Swedish cookies, and Ethel heard her in the living room rallying the others.

They came then, quietly, and Ethel poured. When all had been served, she started another pot of coffee, and took her cup and a cookie—she wasn't hungry—into the living room.

Mrs. Hancock, sitting on the hassock, had a bottle in her hand. On the rug around her were some brushes and one copper pan. "Ladies," she was saying, "now here's something new." Noticing Ethel, Mrs. Hancock picked up the pan. "How'd you like to have this for your kitchen? Here."

Ethel crossed the room. She carried the pan back to where she'd been standing.

"This is no ordinary polish," continued Mrs. Hancock, shaking the bottle vigorously. "This is what is known as liquefied ointment. It possesses rare medicinal properties. It renews wood. It gives you a base for polishing—something to shine that simply wasn't there before. There's nothing like it on the market—not in the polish field. It's a Shipshape product, and you all know what that means." Mrs. Hancock opened the bottle and dabbed at the air. "Note the handy applicator." Snatching a cloth from her lap, she rubbed the leg of the coffee table—"remove all foreign matter first"—and dabbed at the leg with the applicator. "This does for wood what liniment does for horses. It relaxes the grain, injects new life, *soothes* the wood. Well, how do you like it?" she called over to Ethel.

Ethel glanced down at the pan, forgotten in her hand.

"Pass it around," said Mrs. Hancock.

Ethel offered the pan to Mrs. Nilgren, who was nearest.

"I've seen it, thanks."

Ethel moved to the next neighbor.

"I've seen it."

Ethel moved on. "Mrs. Wagner, have you?"

"Many times"—with a smile.

Ethel looked back where she'd been standing before she started out with the pan—and went the other way, finally stepping into the hallway. There she saw a canvas duffle bag on the side of which was embossed a pennant flying the word SHIPSHAPE. And hearing Mrs. Hancock—"And this is new, girls. Can you all see from where you're sitting?"—Ethel began to move again. She kept right on going.

Upstairs, in the bedroom, lying down, she noticed the pan in her hand. She shook it off. It hit the headboard of the bed, denting the traditional mahogany, and came to rest in the satin furrow between Ralph's pillow and hers. Oh, God! In a minute, she'd have to get up and go down to them and do *something* . . . but then she heard the coat hangers banging back empty in the closet downstairs, and the front door opening and, finally, closing. There was a moment of perfect silence in the house before her sudden sob, then another moment, before she heard someone coming, climbing the carpeted stairs.

Ethel foolishly thought it would be Mrs. Wagner, but of course it was Mrs. Hancock, after her pan.

She tiptoed into the room, adjusted the venetian blind, and seated herself lightly on the edge of the bed. "Don't think I don't know how you feel," she said. "Not that it shows yet. I wasn't *sure*, dear." She looked into Ethel's eyes, frightening her.

As though only changing positions, Ethel moved the hand that Mrs. Hancock was after.

"My ointment would fix that, restore the surface," said Mrs. Hancock, her finger searching the little wound in the headboard. She began to explain, gently—like someone with a terrible temper warming up: "When we first started having these little Shipshape parties, they didn't tell each other. They do now, oh yes, or they would if I'd let them. I'm on to them. They're just in it for the mops now. You get one, you know, for having the party in your home. It's collapsible, ideal for the small home or travel. But the truth is you let me down! Why, when you left the room the way you did, you didn't give them any choice. Why, I don't think there's one of that crowd— with the exception of May Wagner—that isn't using one of my free mops! Why, they just walked out on me!"

Ethel, closing her eyes, saw Mrs. Hancock alone, on the hassock, with her products all around her.

"It's a lot of pan for the money," Mrs. Hancock was saying now. She reached over Ethel's body for it. "You'll love your little pan," she said, fondling it.

Ethel's eyes were resisting Mrs. Hancock, but her right hand betrayed her.

"Here?" Mrs. Hancock opened a drawer, took out a purse, and handed it over saying, "Only $12.95."

Ethel found a five and a ten.

"You *do* want the ointment, don't you? The pan and the large bottle come to a little more than this, but it's not enough to worry about."

Mrs. Hancock got up, apparently to leave.

Ethel thought of something. "You do live in Blue Island, don't you?" Ralph would be sure to ask about that—if she had to tell him. And she would!

"Not any more, thank God."

Ethel nodded. She wasn't surprised.

Mrs. Hancock, at the door, peeked out—reminding Ethel of a bored visitor looking for a nurse who would tell her it was time to leave the patient. "I'll leave your ointment and mop downstairs," she said. "I just know everything's going to be all right." Then she smiled and left.

When, toward noon, Ethel heard Ralph come into the driveway, she got out of bed, straightened the spread, and concealed the pan in the closet. She went to the window and gazed down upon the crown of his pearl grey hat. He was carrying a big club of roses.

Questions for Discussion

1. Is Ethel's feeling of insecurity in Blue Island justified?

2. What do the two large pictures suggest about Ethel and Ralph?

3. Does Ethel have any intimation that Mrs. Hancock's motives are ulterior?

4. Are Ethel's neighbors sympathetic to her plight? Are they also victims of Mrs. Hancock?

5. What human values are absent from this community? In what sense is the failure of the community being satirized?

Flannery O'Connor (1925-1964)

Everything That Rises Must Converge

Her doctor had told Julian's mother that she must lose twenty pounds on account of her blood pressure, so on Wednesday nights Julian had to take her downtown on the bus for a reducing class at the Y. The reducing class was designed for working girls over fifty, who weighed from 165 to 200 pounds. His mother was one of the slimmer ones, but she said ladies did not tell their age or weight. She would not ride the buses by herself at night since they had been integrated, and because the reducing class was one of her few pleasures, necessary for her health, and *free*, she said Julian could at least put himself out to take her, considering all she did for him. Julian did not like to consider all she did for him, but every Wednesday night he braced himself and took her.

She was almost ready to go, standing before the hall mirror, putting on her hat, while he, his hands behind him, appeared pinned to the door frame, waiting like Saint Sebastian for the arrows to begin piercing him. The hat was new and had cost her seven dollars and a half. She kept saying, "Maybe I shouldn't have paid that for it. No, I shouldn't have. I'll take it off and return it tomorrow. I shouldn't have bought it."

Julian raised his eyes to heaven. "Yes, you should have bought it," he said. "Put it on and let's go." It was a hideous hat. A purple velvet flap came down on one side of it and stood up on the other; the rest of it was green and looked like a cushion with the stuffing out. He decided it was less comical than jaunty and pathetic. Everything that gave her pleasure was small and depressed him.

She lifted the hat one more time and set it down slowly on top of her head. Two wings of gray hair protruded on either side of her florid face, but her eyes, sky-blue, were as innocent and untouched by experience as they must have been when she was ten. Were it not that she was a widow who had struggled fiercely to feed and clothe and put him through school and who was supporting him still, "until he got on his feet," she might have been a little girl that he had to take to town.

"It's all right, it's all right," he said. "Let's go." He opened the door himself and started down the walk to get her going. The sky was a dying violet and the houses stood out darkly against it, bulbous liver-colored monstrosities of a uniform ugliness though no two were alike. Since this had been a fashionable neighborhood forty years ago, his mother persisted in thinking they did well to have an apartment in it. Each house had a narrow collar of dirt around it in which sat, usually, a grubby child. Julian walked with his hands in his pockets, his head down and thrust forward and his eyes glazed with the determination to make himself completely numb during the time he would be sacrificed to her pleasure.

The door closed and he turned to find the dumpy figure, surmounted by the atrocious hat, coming toward him. "Well," she said, "you only live once and paying a little more for it, I at least won't meet myself coming and going."

"Some day I'll start making money," Julian said gloomily—he knew he never would—"and you can have one of those jokes whenever you take the fit." But first they would move. He visualized a place where the nearest neighbors would be three miles away on either side.

"I think you're doing fine," she said, drawing on her gloves. "You've only been out of school a year. Rome wasn't built in a day."

She was one of the few members of the Y reducing class who arrived in hat and gloves and who had a son who had been to college. "It takes time," she said, "and the world is in such a mess. This hat looked better on me than any of the others, though when she brought it out I said, 'Take that thing back. I wouldn't have it on my head,' and she said, 'Now wait till you see it on,' and when she put it on me, I said, 'We-ull,' and she said, 'If you ask me, that hat does something for you and you do something for the hat, and besides,' she said, 'with that hat, you won't meet yourself coming and going.' "

Julian thought he could have stood his lot better if she had been selfish, if she had been an old hag who drank and screamed at him. He walked along, saturated in depression, as if in the midst of his martyrdom he had lost his faith. Catching sight of his long, hopeless, irritated face, she stopped suddenly with a grief-stricken look, and pulled back on his arm. "Wait on me," she said. "I'm going back to the house and take this thing off and tomorrow I'm going to return it. I was out of my head. I can pay the gas bill with that seven-fifty."

He caught her arm in a vicious grip. "You are not going to take it back," he said. "I like it."

"Well," she said, "I don't think I ought . . ."

"Shut up and enjoy it," he muttered, more depressed than ever.

"With the world in the mess it's in," she said, "it's a wonder we can enjoy anything. I tell you, the bottom rail is on the top."

Julian sighed.

"Of course," she said, "if you know who you are, you can go anywhere." She said this every time he took her to the reducing class. "Most of them in it are not our kind of people," she said, "but I can be gracious to anybody. I know who I am."

"They don't give a damn for your graciousness," Julian said savagely. "Knowing who you are is good for one generation only. You haven't the foggiest idea where you stand now or who you are."

She stopped and allowed her eyes to flash at him. "I most certainly do know who I am," she said, "and if you don't know who you are, I'm ashamed of you."

"Oh hell," Julian said.

"Your great-grandfather was a former governor of this state," she said. "Your grandfather was a prosperous land-owner. Your grandmother was a Godhigh."

"Will you look aound you," he said tensely, "and see where you are now?" and he swept his arm jerkily out to indicate the neighborhood, which the growing darkness at least made less dingy.

"You remain what you are," she said. "Your great-grandfather had a plantation and two hundred slaves."

"There are no more slaves," he said irritably.

"They were better off when they were," she said. He groaned to see that she was off on that topic. She rolled onto it every few days like a train on an open track. He knew every stop, every junction, every swamp along the way, and knew the exact point at which her conclusion would roll majestically into the station: "It's ridiculous. It's simply not realistic. They should rise, yes, but on their own side of the fence."

"Let's skip it," Julian said.

"The ones I feel sorry for," she said, "are the ones that are half white. They're tragic."

"Will you skip it?"

"Suppose we were half white. We would certainly have mixed feelings."

"I have mixed feelings now," he groaned.

"Well let's talk about something pleasant," she said. "I remember going to Grandpa's when I was a little girl. Then the house had double stairways that went up to what was really the second floor—all the cooking was done on the first. I used to like to stay down in the kitchen on account of the way the walls smelled. I would sit with my nose pressed against the plaster and take deep breaths. Actually the place belonged to the Godhighs but your grandfather Chestny paid the mortgage and saved it for them. They were in reduced circumstances," she said, "but reduced or not, they never forgot who they were."

"Doubtless that decayed mansion reminded them," Julian muttered. He never spoke of it without contempt or thought of it without longing. He had seen it once when he was a child before it had been sold. The double stairways had rotted and been torn down. Negroes were living in it. But it remained in his mind as his mother had known it. It appeared in his dreams regularly. He would stand on the wide porch, listening to the rustle of oak leaves, then wander through the high-ceilinged hall into the parlor that opened onto it and gaze at the worn rugs and faded draperies. It occurred to him that it was he, not she, who could have appreciated it. He preferred its threadbare elegance to anything he could name and it was because of it that all the neighborhoods they had lived in had been a torment to him— whereas she had hardly known the difference. She called her insensitivity "being adjustable."

"And I remember the old darky who was my nurse, Caroline. There was no better person in the world. I've always had a great respect for my colored friends," she said. "I'd do anything in the world for them and they'd . . ."

"Will you for God's sake get off that subject?" Julian said. When he got on a bus by himself, he made it a point to sit down beside a Negro, in reparation as it were for his mother's sins.

"You're mighty touchy tonight," she said. "Do you feel all right?"

"Yes I feel all right," he said. "Now lay off."

She pursed her lips. "Well, you certainly are in a vile humor," she observed. "I just won't speak to you at all."

They had reached the bus stop. There was no bus in sight and Julian, his hands still jammed in his pockets and his head thrust forward, scowled down the empty street. The frustration of having to wait on the bus as well as ride on it began to creep up his neck like a hot hand. The presence of his mother was borne in upon him as she gave a pained sigh. He looked at her bleakly. She was holding herself very erect under the preposterous hat, wearing it like a banner of her imaginary dignity. There was in him an evil urge to break her spirit. He suddenly unloosened his tie and pulled it off and put it in his pocket.

She stiffened. "Why must you look like *that* when you take me to town?" she said. "Why must you deliberately embarrass me?"

"If you'll never learn where you are," he said, "you can at least learn where I am."

"You look like a—thug," she said.

"Then I must be one," he murmured.

"I'll just go home," she said. "I will not bother you. If you can't do a little thing like that for me . . ."

Rolling his eyes upward, he put his tie back on. "Restored to my class," he muttered. He thrust his face toward her and hissed, "True culture is in the mind, the *mind*," he said and tapped his head, "the mind."

"It's in the heart," she said, "and in how you do things and how you do things is because of who you *are*."

"Nobody in the damn bus cares who you are."

"I care who I am," she said icily.

The lighted bus appeared on top of the next hill and as it approached, they moved out into the street to meet it. He put his hand under her elbow and hoisted her up on the creaking step. She entered with a little smile, as if she were going into a drawing room where everyone had been waiting for her. While he put in the tokens, she sat down on one of the broad front seats for three which faced the aisle. A thin woman with protruding teeth and long yellow hair was sitting on the end of it. His mother moved up beside her and left room for Julian beside herself. He sat down and looked at the floor across the aisle where a pair of thin feet in red and white canvas sandals were planted.

His mother immediately began a general conversation meant to attract anyone who felt like talking. "Can it get any hotter?" she said and removed from her purse a folding fan, black with a Japanese scene on it, which she began to flutter before her.

"I reckon it might could," the woman with the protruding teeth said, "but I know for a fact my apartment couldn't get no hotter."

"It must get the afternoon sun," his mother said. She sat forward and looked up and down the bus. It was half filled. Everybody was white. "I see we have the bus to ourselves," she said. Julian cringed.

"For a change," said the woman across the aisle, the owner of the red and white canvas sandals. "I come on one the other day and they were thick as fleas—up front and all through."

"The world is in a mess everywhere," his mother said. "I don't know how we've let it get in this fix."

"What gets my goat is all those boys from good families stealing automobile tires," the woman with the protruding teeth said. "I told my boy, I said you may not be rich but you been raised right and if I ever catch you in any such mess, they can send you on to the reformatory. Be exactly where you belong."

"Training tells," his mother said. "Is your boy in high school?"

"Ninth grade," the woman said.

"My son just finished college last year. He wants to write but he's selling typewriters until he gets started," his mother said.

The woman leaned forward and peered at Julian. He threw her such a malevolent look that she subsided against the seat. On the floor across the aisle there was an abandoned newspaper. He got up and got it and opened it out in front of him. His mother discreetly continued the conversation in a lower tone but the woman across the aisle said in a loud voice, "Well that's nice. Selling typewriters is close to writing. He can go right from one to the other."

"I tell him," his mother said, "that Rome wasn't built in a day."

Behind the newspaper Julian was withdrawing into the inner compartment of his mind where he spent most of his time. This was a kind of mental bubble in which he established himself when he could not bear to be a part of what was going on around him. From it he could see out and judge but in it he was safe from any kind of penetration from without. It was the only place where he felt free of the general idiocy of his fellows. His mother had never entered it but from it he could see her with absolute clarity.

The old lady was clever enough and he thought that if she had started from any of the right premises, more might have been expected of her. She lived according to the laws of her own fantasy world, outside of which he had never seen her set foot. The law of it was to sacrifice herself for him after she had first created the necessity to do so by making a mess of things. If he had permitted her sacrifices, it was only because her lack of foresight had made them necessary. All of her life had been a struggle to act like a Chestny without the Chestny goods, and to give him everything she thought a Chestny ought to have; but since, said she, it was fun to struggle, why complain? And when you had won, as she had won, what fun to look back on the hard times! He could not forgive her that she had enjoyed the struggle and that she thought *she* had won.

What she meant when she said she had won was that she had brought him up successfully and had sent him to college and that he had turned out so well—good looking (her teeth had gone unfilled so that his could be straightened), intelligent (he realized he was too intelligent to be a success), and with a future ahead of him (there was of course no future ahead of him). She excused his gloominess on the grounds that he was still growing up and his radical ideas on his lack of practical experience. She said he didn't yet know a thing about "life," that he hadn't even entered the real world— when already he was as disenchanted with it as a man of fifty.

The further irony of all this was that in spite of her, he had turned out so well. In spite of going to only a third-rate college, he had, on his own initiative, come out with a first-rate education; in spite of growing up dominated by a small mind, he had ended up with a large one; in spite of all her foolish views, he was free of prejudice and unafraid to face facts. Most miraculous of all, instead of being blinded by love for her as she was for him, he had cut himself emotionally free of her and could see her with complete objectivity. He was not dominated by his mother.

The bus stopped with a sudden jerk and shook him from his meditation. A woman from the back lurched forward with little steps and barely escaped falling in his newspaper as she righted herself. She got off and a large Negro got on. Julian kept his paper lowered to watch. It gave him a certain satisfaction to see injustice in daily operation. It confirmed his view that with a few exceptions there was no one worth knowing within a radius of three hundred miles. The Negro was well dressed and carried a briefcase. He looked around and then sat down on the other end of the seat where the woman with the red and white canvas sandals was sitting. He immediately unfolded a newspaper and obscured himself behind it. Julian's mother's elbow at once prodded insistently into his ribs. "Now you see why I won't ride on these buses by myself," she whispered.

The woman with the red and white canvas sandals had risen at the same time the Negro sat down and had gone further back in the bus and taken the seat of the woman who had got off. His mother leaned forward and cast her an approving look.

Julian rose, crossed the aisle, and sat down in the place of the woman with the canvas sandals. From this position, he looked serenely across at his mother. Her face had turned an angry red. He stared at her, making his eyes the eyes of a stranger. He felt his tension suddenly lift as if he had openly declared war on her.

He would have liked to get in conversation with the Negro and to talk with him about art or politics or any subject that would be above the comprehension of those around them, but the man remained entrenched behind his paper. He was either ignoring the change of seating or had never noticed it. There was no way for Julian to convey his sympathy.

His mother kept her eyes fixed reproachfully on his face. The woman with the protruding teeth was looking at him avidly as if he were a type of monster new to her.

"Do you have a light?" he asked the Negro.

Without looking away from his paper, the man reached in his pocket and handed him a packet of matches.

"Thanks," Julian said. For a moment he held the matches foolishly. A NO SMOKING sign looked down upon him from over the door. This alone would not have deterred him; he had no cigarettes. He had quit smoking some months before because he could not afford it. "Sorry," he muttered and handed back the matches. The Negro lowered the paper and gave him an annoyed look. He took the matches and raised the paper again.

His mother continued to gaze at him but she did not take advantage of his momentary discomfort. Her eyes retained their battered look. Her face seemed to be unnaturally red, as if her blood pressure had risen. Julian allowed no glimmer of sympathy to show on his face. Having got the advantage, he wanted desperately to keep it and carry it through. He would have liked to teach her a lesson that would last her a while, but there seemed no way to continue the point. The Negro refused to come out from behind his paper.

Julian folded his arms and looked stolidly before him, facing her but as if he did not see her, as if he had ceased to recognize her existence. He visualized a scene in which, the bus having reached their stop, he would remain in his seat and when she said, "Aren't you going to get off?" he would look at her as at a stranger who had rashly addressed him. The corner they got off on was usually deserted, but it was well lighted and it would not hurt her to walk by herself the four blocks to the Y. He decided to wait until the time came and then decide whether or not he would let her get off by herself. He would have to be at the Y at ten to bring her back, but he could leave her wondering if he was going to show up. There was no reason for her to think she could always depend on him.

He retired again into the high-ceilinged room sparsely settled with large pieces of antique furniture. His soul expanded momentarily but then he became aware of his mother across from him and the vision shriveled. He studied her coldly. Her feet in little pumps dangled like a child's and did not quite reach the floor. She was training on him an exaggerated look of reproach. He felt completely detached from her. At that moment he could with pleasure have slapped her as he would have slapped a particularly obnoxious child in his charge.

He began to imagine various unlikely ways by which he could teach her a lesson. He might make friends with some distinguished Negro professor or lawyer and bring him home to spend the evening. He would be entirely justified but her blood pressure would rise to 300. He could not push her to the extent of making her have a stroke, and moreover, he had never been successful at making any Negro friends. He had tried to strike up an acquaintance on the bus with some of the better types, with ones that looked like professors or ministers or lawyers. One morning he had sat down next to a distinguished-looking dark brown man who had answered his questions with a sonorous solemnity but who had turned out to be an undertaker. Another day he had sat down beside a cigar-smoking Negro with a diamond ring on his finger, but after a few stilted pleasantries, the Negro had rung the buzzer and risen, slipping two lottery tickets into Julian's hand as he climbed over him to leave.

He imagined his mother lying desperately ill and his being able to secure only a Negro doctor for her. He toyed with that idea for a few minutes and then dropped it for a momentary vision of himself participating as a sympathizer in a sit-in demonstration. This was possible but he did not linger with it. Instead, he approached the ultimate horror. He brought home a beautiful suspiciously Negroid woman. Prepare yourself, he said. There is nothing you can do about it. This is the woman I've chosen. She's intelligent, dignified, even good, and she's suffered, and she hasn't thought it *fun*. Now persecute us, go ahead and persecute us. Drive her out of here, but remember, you're driving me too. His eyes were narrowed and through the indignation he had generated, he saw his mother across the aisle, purple-faced, shrunken to the dwarf-like proportions of her moral nature, sitting like a mummy beneath the ridiculous banner of her hat.

He was tilted out of his fantasy again as the bus stopped. The door opened with a sucking hiss and out of the dark a large, gaily dressed, sullen-looking colored woman got on with a little boy. The child, who might have been four, had on a short plaid suit and a Tyrolean hat with a blue feather in it. Julian hoped that he would sit down beside him and that the woman would push in beside his mother. He could think of no better arrangement.

As she waited for her tokens, the woman was surveying the seating possibilities—he hoped with the idea of sitting where she was least wanted. There was something familiar-looking about her but Julian could not place what it was. She was a giant of a woman. Her face was set not only to meet opposition but to seek it out. The downward tilt of her large lower lip was like a warning sign: DON'T TAMPER WITH ME. Her bulging figure was encased in a green crepe dress and her feet overflowed in red shoes. She had on a hideous hat. A purple velvet flap came down on one side of it and stood up on the other; the rest of it was green and looked like a cushion with the stuffing out. She carried a mammoth red pocketbook that bulged throughout as if it were stuffed with rocks.

To Julian's disappointment, the little boy climbed up on the empty seat beside his mother. His mother lumped all children, black and white, into the common category, "cute," and she thought little Negroes were on the whole cuter than little white children. She smiled at the little boy as he climbed on the seat.

Meanwhile the woman was bearing down upon the empty seat beside Julian. To his annoyance, she squeezed herself into it. He saw his mother's face change as the woman settled herself next to him and he realized with satisfaction that this was more objectionable to her than it was to him. Her face seemed almost gray and there was a look of dull recognition in her eyes, as if suddenly she had sickened at some awful confrontation. Julian saw that it was because she and the woman had, in a sense, swapped sons. Though his mother would not realize the symbolic significance of this, she would feel it. His amusement showed plainly on his face.

The woman next to him muttered something unintelligible to herself. He was conscious of a kind of bristling next to him, a muted growling like that of an angry cat. He could not see anything but the red pocketbook upright on the bulging green thighs. He visualized the woman as she had stood waiting for her tokens—the ponderous figure, rising from the red shoes upward over the solid hips, the mammoth bosom, the haughty face, to the green and purple hat.

His eyes widened.

The vision of the two hats, identical, broke upon him with the radiance of a brilliant sunrise. His face was suddenly lit with joy. He could not believe that Fate had thrust upon his mother such a lesson. He gave a loud chuckle so that she would look at him and see that he saw. She turned her eyes on him slowly. The blue in them seemed to have turned a bruised purple. For a moment he had an uncomfortable sense of her innocence, but it lasted only a second before principle rescued him. Justice entitled him to laugh. His grin hardened until it said to her as plainly as if he were saying aloud: Your punishment exactly fits your pettiness. This should teach you a permanent lesson.

Her eyes shifted to the woman. She seemed unable to bear looking at him and to find the woman preferable. He became conscious again of the bristling presence at his side. The woman was rumbling like a volcano about to become active. His mother's mouth began to twitch slightly at one corner. With a sinking heart, he saw incipient signs of recovery on her face and realized that this was going to strike her suddenly as funny and was going to be no lesson at all. She kept her eyes on the woman and an amused smile came over her face as if the woman were a monkey that had stolen her hat. The little Negro was looking up at her with large fascinated eyes. He had been trying to attract her attention for some time.

"Carver!" the woman said suddenly. "Come heah!"

When he saw that the spotlight was on him at last, Carver drew his feet up and turned himself toward Julian's mother and giggled.

"Carver!" the woman said. "You heah me? Come heah!"

Carver slid down from the seat but remained squatting with his back against the base of it, his head turned slyly around toward Julian's mother, who was smiling at him. The woman reached a hand across the aisle and snatched him to her. He righted himself and hung backwards on her knees, grinning at Julian's mother. "Isn't he cute?" Julian's mother said to the woman with the protruding teeth.

"I reckon he is," the woman said without conviction.

The Negress yanked him upright but he eased out of her grip and shot across the aisle and scrambled, giggling wildly, onto the seat beside his love.

"I think he likes me," Julian's mother said, and smiled at the woman. It was the smile she used when she was being particularly gracious to an inferior. Julian saw everything lost. The lesson had rolled off her like rain on a roof.

The woman stood up and yanked the little boy off the seat as if she were snatching him from contagion. Julian could feel the rage in her at having no weapon like his mother's smile. She gave the child a sharp slap across his leg. He howled once and then thrust his head into her stomach and kicked his feet against her shins. "Be-have," she said vehemently.

The bus stopped and the Negro who had been reading the newspaper got off. The woman moved over and set the little boy down with a thump between herself and Julian. She held him firmly by the knee. In a moment he put his hands in front of his face and peeped at Julian's mother through his fingers.

"I see yoooooooo!" she said and put her hand in front of her face and peeped at him.

The woman slapped his hand down. "Quit yo' foolishness," she said, "before I knock the living Jesus out of you!"

Julian was thankful that the next stop was theirs. He reached up and pulled the cord. The woman reached up and pulled it at the same time. Oh my God, he thought. He had the terrible intuition that when they got off the bus together, his mother would open her purse and give the little boy a nickel. The gesture would be as natural to her as breathing. The bus stopped and the woman got up and lunged to the front, dragging the child, who wished to stay on, after her. Julian and his mother got up and followed. As they neared the door, Julian tried to relieve her of her pocketbook.

"No," she murmured, "I want to give the little boy a nickel."

"No!" Julian hissed. "No!"

She smiled down at the child and opened her bag. The bus door opened and the woman picked him up by the arm and descended with him, hanging at her hip. Once in the street she set him down and shook him.

Julian's mother had to close her purse while she got down the bus step but as soon as her feet were on the ground, she opened it again and began to rummage inside. "I can't find but a penny," she whispered, "but it looks like a new one."

"Don't do it!" Julian said fiercely between his teeth. There was a street-light on the corner and she hurried to get under it so that she could better see into her pocketbook. The woman was heading off rapidly down the street with the child still hanging backward on her hand.

"Oh little boy!" Julian's mother called and took a few quick steps and caught up with them just beyond the lamp-post. "Here's a bright new penny for you," and she held out the coin, which shone bronze in the dim light.

The huge woman turned and for a moment stood, her shoulders lifted and her face frozen with frustrated rage, and stared at Julian's mother. Then all at once she seemed to explode like a piece of machinery that had been given one ounce of pressure too much. Julian saw the black fist swing out with the red pocketbook. He shut his eyes and cringed as he heard the woman shout, "He don't take nobody's pennies!" When he opened his eyes, the woman was disappearing down the street with the little boy staring wide-eyed over her shoulder. Julian's mother was sitting on the sidewalk.

"I told you not to do that," Julian said angrily. "I told you not to do that!"

He stood over her for a minute, gritting his teeth. Her legs were stretched out in front of her and her hat was on her lap. He squatted down and looked her in the face. It was totally expressionless. "You got exactly what you deserved," he said. "Now get up."

He picked up her pocketbook and put what had fallen out back in it. He picked the hat up off her lap. The penny caught his eye on the sidewalk and he picked that up and let it drop before her eyes into the purse. Then he stood up and leaned over and held his hands out to pull her up. She remained immobile. He sighed. Rising above them on either side were black apartment buildings, marked with irregular rectangles of light. At the end of the block a man came out of a door and walked off in the opposite direction. "All right," he said, "suppose somebody happens by and wants to know why you're sitting on the sidewalk?"

She took the hand and, breathing hard, pulled heavily up on it and then stood for a moment, swaying slightly as if the spots of light in the darkness were circling around her. Her eyes, shadowed and confused, finally settled on his face. He did not try to conceal his irritation. "I hope this teaches you a lesson," he said. She leaned forward and her eyes raked his face. She seemed trying to determine his identity. Then, as if she found nothing familiar about him, she started off with a headlong movement in the wrong direction.

"Aren't you going on to the Y?" he asked.

"Home," she muttered.

"Well, are we walking?"

For answer she kept going. Julian followed along, his hands behind him. He saw no reason to let the lesson she had had go without backing it up with an explanation of its meaning. She might as well be made to understand what had happened to her. "Don't think that was just an uppity Negro woman," he said. "That was the whole colored race which will no longer take your condescending pennies. That was your black double. She can wear the same hat as you, and to be sure," he added gratuitously (because he thought it was funny), "it looked better on her than it did on you. What all this means," he said, "is that the old world is gone. The old manners are obsolete and your graciousness is not worth a damn." He thought bitterly of the house that had been lost for him. "You aren't who you think you are," he said.

She continued to plow ahead, paying no attention to him. Her hair had come undone on one side. She dropped her pocketbook and took no notice. He stooped and picked it up and handed it to her but she did not take it.

"You needn't act as if the world had come to an end," he said, "because it hasn't. From now on you've got to live in a new world and face a few realities for a change. Buck up," he said, "it won't kill you."

She was breathing fast.

"Let's wait on the bus," he said.

"Home," she said thickly.

"I hate to see you behave like this," he said. "Just like a child. I should be able to expect more of you." He decided to stop where he was and make her stop and wait for a bus. "I'm not going any farther," he said, stopping. "We're going on the bus."

She continued to go on as if she had not heard him. He took a few steps and caught her arm and stopped her. He looked into her face and caught his breath. He was looking into a face he had never seen before. "Tell Grandpa to come get me," she said.

He stared, stricken.

"Tell Caroline to come get me," she said.

Stunned, he let her go and she lurched forward again, walking as if one leg were shorter than the other. A tide of darkness seemed to be sweeping her from him. "Mother!" he cried. "Darling, sweetheart, wait!" Crumpling, she fell to the pavement. He dashed forward and fell at her side, crying, "Mamma, Mamma!" He turned her over. Her face was fiercely distorted. One eye, large and staring, moved slightly to the left as if it had become unmoored. The other remained fixed on him, raked his face again, found nothing and closed.

"Wait here, wait here!" he cried and jumped up and began to run for help toward a cluster of lights he saw in the distance ahead of him. "Help, help!" he shouted, but his voice was thin, scarcely a thread of sound. The lights drifted farther away the faster he ran and his feet moved numbly as if they carried him nowhere. The tide of darkness seemed to sweep him back to her, postponing from moment to moment his entry into the world of guilt and sorrow.

Questions for Discussion

1. The story is told from Julian's point of view. Are we getting an "objective" account of this incident?

2. To what extent are Julian's attitudes inherited from his mother?

3. Why is Julian interested in conversation "about art or politics" with Negroes?

4. Julian is in a sense a satirist—one who criticizes the world's failures. To what extent is he satirized by the author?

5. The title is drawn from the late Teihard de Chardin, a theologian-biologist. One critic has said that the story shows ". . . young and old and black and white to be practically sealed off against one another, struggling but hardly upward or together in a welter of petty feelings and cross purposes, resolved only slightly even by the tragic blow." Do you agree with this interpretation?

6. In what ways is the world of this story like the world of "Blue Island"?

Biographical Notes

Horace (65-8 B.C.), the son of a minor government official, was educated both in Rome and Athens. Upon the death of Caesar in 44 B.C. he joined the army of Junius Brutus to fight against Mark Antony and Octavius Caesar. After the war he became a clerk in Rome, where he started writing poetry and formed a friendship with Virgil. The great epic poet introduced him to the patron Maecenas, whose name became a symbol in literary history for a wealthy and sympathetic supporter of artists. Generously provided for, Horace wrote steadily in both the lyric and satiric forms (a number of his poems were commissioned by the Emperor Augustus) and covered a wide range of subjects from the pleasures of living in the country to Roman history and the foibles of human nature. His satire is on the whole less severe and vigorous than that of Juvenal and less complex and obscure than that of Persius.

Juvenal (ca. 60-ca. 140), one of the three great satirists of Latin literature (Horace and Persius are the other two) is difficult to write about with any certainty. While it is true he was known to Martial and other poets during the reigns of Trajan and Hadrian, little verifiable information about him has come down to us. Perhaps he was a man embittered and disillusioned with the Roman society in which he lived. At any rate, his sixteen *Satires* are an impressive series of attacks on the abuses and follies of the Rome of his age. He was admired and imitated by a number of English satirists, including Marston and Donne in the Elizabethan Age and Dryden and Johnson in the neo-classical period.

William Shakespeare (1564-1616) was born in Stratford-on-Avon and educated in the Stratford Grammar School. Probably by 1588 he was in London as an actor, and by 1594 he was a member of the Lord Chamberlain's Men (later the King's Men), the most successful company of the day. He was the principal playwright for this group, who performed in their own Globe Theater for many years. By the time he wrote *King Lear*, about 1605, he had had a long experience in writing poetic drama. After the period of his great tragedies he wrote his final series of plays, which culminated in *The Tempest* (1611). Earlier he had composed a remarkable sequence of 154 sonnets—remarkable because of their variations on the traditional Petrarchan themes. They were published in 1609.

John Donne (1572-1631), one of the masters of the paradox in verse and prose, was a paradox himself. Born a Roman Catholic, he left the church

210

and was ordained an Anglo-Catholic minister in 1615 and later appointed Dean of St. Paul's. A writer of satire (based on classical models) and witty love poems in the 1590's, he went on to compose some of the most passionate and intellectually complex religious poetry as well as some of the most outstanding sermons of the 17th Century. Although only a few of his poems were published in his lifetime, he influenced a number of younger poets who knew his work only in manuscript. An edition of his poems appeared posthumously in 1633.

Jean de la Fontaine (1621-1695) was born in Château-Thierry and educated at the college of Reims. After a number of years as a deputy ranger in charge of the forests and streams of his native duchy, he entered upon a literary career with the publication in 1654 of an adaptation of the Roman playwright Terence's *Eunuchus*. He established his reputation with *Contes et Nouvelles en Verse* (1664). Eventually he settled in Paris as a poet and became associated with Boileau, Molière, and Racine during the Golden Age of Louis XIV (1638-1715). His famous *Fables* were published in two sets in 1668 and 1678.

Molière (1622-1673) was born Jean Baptiste Poquelin in Paris, where he studied law and philosophy. Although encouraged to enter his father's upholstery business, he took up the profession of an actor and toured France. His company became so famous it was asked to appear before Louis XIV, who subsequently permitted the troupe to settle at the Palais-Royal Theater. Here Molière worked for the rest of his life as an actor and playwright. Like Shakespeare his knowledge of the theater came from practical experience. His most important plays are *The Misanthrope* (1666), *Tartuffe* (1667), *The Miser* (1668), and *The Would-Be Gentleman* (1671). He died while acting in his last play *The Imaginary Invalid* and was given church burial only after the King intervened, since an actor at the time was considered an immoral person.

Alexander Pope (1688-1744) was the son of a wealthy London merchant. This advantage, however, was offset by two serious disadvantages: his Roman Catholicism, which prevented him from attending a university, and tuberculosis of the spine, which left him a dwarf. Despite these handicaps he managed to become the first English writer to make a living solely through literature (principally through his translations of the *Iliad* and the *Odyssey*) and the most brilliant satirist in the language. In addition to *The*

Rape of the Lock (the second version included in this anthology was published in 1714) he also wrote *The Dunciad* (1728) in which he attacked his literary opponents as well as the commercial corruption and the lowering of taste throughout England. His *Essay on Criticism* (1711), arguing for the literary principles of neo-classicism, and his *Essay on Man* (1733), arguing for the tenets of Deism, are his best known works other than his satires.

Jonathan Swift (1677-1745), the son of English parents, was born in Dublin a few months after the death of his father and educated by his uncle at Trinity College. First employed as a secretary by Sir William Temple in 1689 (through whom he met Esther Johnson, the famous Stella in his life), he left the household of his kinsman in 1699 to enter a varied career both as an Anglican clergyman and a political polemist. His first important work as a satirist appeared in 1704 with the publication of *The Tale of a Tub* and *The Battle of the Books*. After serving first the Whig and then the Tory parties he left the political scene in 1713 to become Dean of St. Patrick's Cathedral in Dublin. Here he lived the rest of his life attacking mankind in general and English policies in particular. *Gulliver's Travels* (1726) grew out of his hatred for the unreasonableness of man, "the most pernicious Race of little odious Vermin that Nature ever suffered to crawl upon the Surface of the Earth." *A Modest Proposal* (1729) stemmed from his sympathy for the Irish who were being oppressed by the English.

Voltaire (1694-1778), whose real name was François-Marie Arouet, was educated at a Jesuit school in Paris. His literary success came early with various political satires (which in one case brought him eleven months' imprisonment); a tragedy, *Oedipe* (1718); and an epic, *La Henriade* (1723). The range of his work was large. After another term in prison he spent three years in England, where he was impressed by the more tolerant system of government. His criticism of the French government and church was far-reaching and made prolonged residence in France difficult. At one point he lived in the court of Frederick the Great of Prussia, but eventually he settled down in Switzerland. It was during this period that he wrote *Candide* (1759) and the *Philosophical Dictionary* (1764).

Robert Burns (1759-1796) was born in Alloway, Ayrshire, Scotland, the son of an impoverished tenant farmer. Though he had little formal schooling, he was well-read in poetry, theology, and philosophy and was not the primitive poet of nature he led his public to believe. Reacting against his Calvinist upbringing, he cultivated liberal views in politics and theology and lived a wildly irregular life, fathering a number of illegitimate children, all to the dismay of his Presbyterian countrymen. His first volume, *Poems Chiefly in the Scottish Dialect* (1786), enjoyed extraordinary success in intellectual Edinburgh as well as in London. It should be noted that Burns was a satirist in the native tradition of Scottish poetry which owed very little to the neo-classicism of Dryden and Pope. *Tam O'Shanter* (1790), a mock-heroic poem, is his most ambitious satire.

William Blake (1757-1827) was the son of a London haberdasher and his only formal education was at the school of the Royal Academy of Art. He was an engraver by trade. Although he was one of the outstanding English artists, he was late acquiring his reputation. His poetry is intimately connected with his pictorial work; indeed his books are highly visual, a fusion of text and design. His first book was *Poetical Sketches* (1783). *Songs of Innocence* came in 1789 and its counterpart *Songs of Experience* in 1794, from which "London" is taken. His later work is the long "prophetic" poems of a Biblical character.

John Betjeman (1906———), who was educated at Oxford, is an architectural critic as well as a poet. Although a friend of Eliot and Auden, he is not a "modernist" poet, but he has wittily used the verse forms of Hardy and other late Victorians to render the contemporary English scene. His books include *Mount Zion* (1933), *New Bats in Old Belfries* (1949), *A Few Late Chrysanthemums* (1954), and *Collected Poems* (1958).

J. F. Powers (1917———) was born in Jacksonville, Illinois. He attended the Chicago branch of Northwestern University. His short stories, which have been widely admired, have appeared in two collections: *The Prince of Darkness and Other Stories* (1947) and *The Presence of Grace* (1956). His most recent work is a novel, *Morte D'Urban* (1962).

Flannery O'Connor (1925-1964) was born in Savannah, Georgia, and spent most of her life in Milledgeville in that state. She was educated at the Georgia State College for Women and the State University of Iowa. She wrote two books of short stories, *A Good Man is Hard to Find* (1955) and *Everything That Rises Must Converge* (1965), and two novels, *Wise Blood* (1952) and *The Violent Bear It Away* (1960).